"HERE'S THE BABY. PRETTY DEAR!"

THOMAS BAILEY ALDRICH, EDITOR-IN-CHIEF

THE
MERRY MAKER

EDITED BY

Joel Chandler Harris

AUXILIARY EDUCATIONAL LEAGUE

CHICAGO   1952

PRINTED AND BOUND IN THE U. S. A. BY
KINGSPORT PRESS, INC., KINGSPORT, TENN.

CONTENTS

Contents

THE MERRY MAKER

Funny Leaves for the Younger Branches

BY

BARON KRAKEMSIDES OF BURSTENOUDELAFEN

ILLUSTRATED BY ALFRED CROWQUILL

YOUNGER BRANCHES:

He who creates laughter creates happiness — come then and laugh at my doings and appreciate me! for where one is found willing and capable to do so, thousands are found whose only pleasure is to make you cry! Laughter is your privilege! come then and enjoy it; ring a chime of merry little laughs that shall be heard afar off, and cheer the hearts of those that love you! I love you! I therefore dedicate my pen to you, and in this my book draw upon you for thousands of laughs! and be sure you honor my draughts as you all have a great fund at your disposal.

Yours affectionately,

KRAKEMSIDES.

CASTLE OF BURSTENOUDELAFEN.

FUNNY LEAVES FOR THE YOUNGER BRANCHES

MR. TIM RESOLVES ON SPORT.

"I'll have some sport," said Mr. Tim,
  "Like hunters of renown;
I'll slaughter them both right and left,
  Egad I'll bring them down."
He smiled, and smiling went to
    sleep,
  With thoughts of shedding
    blood;
He woke! and found the
    sun was up;
    In glorious golden flood!
  He took some bullets, round and large,
    And gun with ample bore;
  And took his powder, fine and strong,
    With sandwiches a store;
  He took his little cross-bred dog,
    To hunt the covers round;
  Then dived into the tangled wood,
    Where elephants were found.

3

HE DOES SEE AN ELEPHANT.

With stealthy tread and wary peep,
    Each shady nook he passed ;
With eyes and ears distended wide,
    He clutched his weapon fast ;
When, ah ! he heard a heavy tread,
        That made the dead wood crack,
    And made him shrink within
        himself,
        And draw his body back.
    It was a monstrous elephant,
        Which caused his fear and dread,
    That fed upon the waving leaves,
    Far, far above his head.
More like a mountain than a beast
    That elephant appeared,
As ever and anon, in sport,
    Its pliant trunk it reared.

HIS DISMAY.

His little dog just gave a
    growl
Of fright and fear com-
    bined,
With teeth all showing
    in a row,
        And tail tucked in behind.
    The elephant sent forth a cry,
        And flapped his monstrous ears,

As if to say, " Who is it with
  My breakfast interferes ? "
Off, like a shot, the puppy ran
  With ears and tail forlorn,
And Tim was after in a trice,
  To see where he was gone.
The elephant went dashing on
  Through trees both great and small,
With lifted trunk and thrilling cry,
  Like some great clarion's call.

TIM PONDERS AND RESOLVES.

Tim followed him — but with his eyes —
  Into the darksome wood;
Then scratched his head and rubbed his
    chin
  In contemplative mood.
But, soon resolved, he climbed a rock,
  From which, with safety, he
Might peep, and see the whereabouts
  That elephant might be.
Adzooks ! he saw him sure enough,
  And many more beside,
All browzing on the tender leaves,
  Quite friendly, side by side.

HE FIRES.

He raised his deadly barrel straight
  Without one single pang,
And fired right amidst the lot
  With one tremendous bang !

Down went the brute, and down went Tim,
   All lengthways on his back,
      He felt annihilated quite,
        He came down such a whack!
Off ran the drove, with screaming cries,
      Through brake, and brier and fell,
    With footsteps thund'ring on the earth,
      They startled all the dell.
But one poor thing, left moaning
        there,
      With little life to boast,
    Just rolled its filmy eyes around,
      And then gave up the ghost.
Then Tim set up and looked around
   With idiotic stare,
And wondering very much at what
   He had been doing there.

HE ADMIRES HIS GAME.

He rose, then round and round
   the brute
He walked with wondr'ing
   eye,
And thought to carry such a
   load

      Would all his strength defy.
    He pulled it by its massive trunk,
      He pulled it by its tail;
    He put out all his puny strength,
      But all of no avail:

He might as well have tried to move
　　The mountains by its side;
And thus he found that he must lose
　　The homage to his pride.
Who would believe he'd done the deed?
　　Who would not say, " No go ! "
For if he could not take it home,
　　He had no proof to show.

HE IS TAKEN BY SURPRISE.

So once again he tried his force,
　　With all his power put,
He could as well have raised the earth, —
　　It did not move a foot.
Just in the midst a roar was
　　heard,
　　That rolled across the plain,
Made by a brute " just
　　twice as big "
　　As that great one he'd
　　slain.
With rolling eyes it glared
　　on Tim,
　　　　Enough his blood to freeze,
　　　　And all his courage dying out,
　　　　He sank upon his knees.

REVENGE.

With rapid twist he seized poor Tim
　　Around his slender waist,

Then opened wide his caverned mouth,
To grind him into paste.

'Oh, deary me! Oh gra-
cious me!
'Oh, heavens what a
fate!'"
Cried Tim, when at his
cries the brute
Appeared to hesitate;
Then slowly rolled him
tighter up—

Ah! very tight indeed,
Then, like an engine, off he set
Across the plains at speed!

TORTURE.

He stopped upon a rocky cliff,
    Where you might see below
The sea roll high with dinning
        noise,
    With foam like driven snow.
He dangled here, he dangled there,
    He dangled to and fro,
He every moment felt the trunk
        Preparing to let go.
    When just as he thought all was up,
        When he from life must pass,
    The brute quite coolly turned him round,
        And sat him on the grass.

THEY TRY HIM.

Oh, horrid sight! from either side,
　　From hill and dale and wood,
Came trotting up with might and main,
　　An elephantine brood.
They soon arrange a rural court,
　　Where he was to be tried,
For having been found in the act
　　Of El-e-phan-ti-cide.

They argued this, they argued that,
　　They argued well indeed;
But yet they could not argue that
　　Tim had not done the deed.

THE VERDICT.

Up rose the Judge — an Elephant
   Of sage and solemn look,
And gave the verdict just as if
   He'd read it in a book;
"Man, man," said he, "who judge
   your kind
By laws thought wise and good,
   Declare that it is right and just
To claim man's blood for blood.
Now we, though brutes despised by you,
   To you a lesson give,
Nor like revenge make justice seem,
   So do decree, — you live !
But far from all your fellow men, —
   These wilds must be your fate;
And thus the murder of our friend
   Alone you'll expiate!"
Tim fainted at the dread decree,
   And lay like mutton dead;
For, ah, he felt too well the force
   Of all that wise brute said.

THE FLIGHT.

Half frenzied by his dreadful fate,
   He started up to flee,
And soon beyond his guards he fled,
   And gained a neighbouring tree.

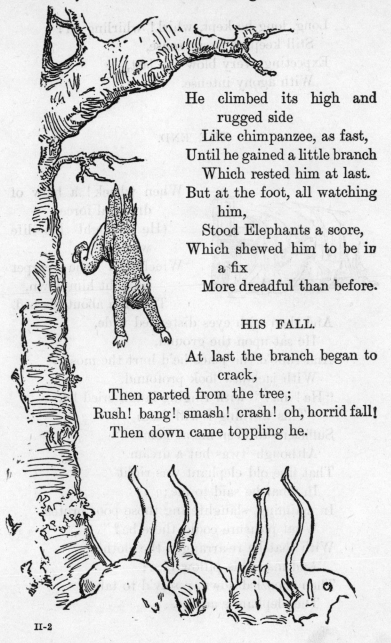

He climbed its high and
    rugged side
Like chimpanzee, as fast,
Until he gained a little branch
    Which rested him at last.
But at the foot, all watching
    him,
    Stood Elephants a score,
Which shewed him to be in
    a fix
    More dreadful than before.

HIS FALL.

At last the branch began to
    crack,
    Then parted from the tree;
Rush! bang! smash! crash! oh, horrid fall!
    Then down came toppling he.

Long, long he kept, whirl! whirling on!
  Still keeping every sense,
Expecting every blow the last,
  With agony intense.

THE END.

When whack! a blow of
  dreadful force,
  (He thought his life
    was sped)
Which on the carpet
  brought him down,
That ran about his bed.

And then with eyes distended wide,
  He sat upon the ground,
And rubb'd the place he'd hurt the most,
  With jackdaw look profound.
"Ha! ha!" with ringing laugh cried he,
  "This warning I will deem
Sufficient to keep me at home,
  Although 'twas but a dream.
That fine old elephant was right
  In what he said to me;
In maiming, slaughtering those poor brutes,
  What pleasure could there be?"
With that he re-arranged the clothes,
  And made his pillow nice;
Then snoozled down, resolv'd to take
  The elephant's advice.

THE DRAGON'S STORY

By TUDOR JENKS.

(FROM HIS "IMAGINOTIONS.")

MAMA, please tell us a story!" cried all the young dragons.

"Children, do be less noisy!" said their father, the Honorable Samuel P. Dragon. He had slain a knight that very evening and was perhaps a little irritable. Young dragons should be thoughtful, and should never disturb their parents after the night's fighting is over.

"Hush, children!" said Mrs. Dragon. "Your father has to fight hard all night, and in the day he needs his rest. I will tell you one nice story, if you will promise to go quietly to bed afterward."

The youngsters coiled down into comfortable hollows in the rock, and Mrs. Dragon prepared to begin her story.

"I suppose you would prefer a man-story?"

"Please, Mama. We are *so* tired of ' When I was a little dragon.' Tell us a real man-story; but be sure not to have the dragon hurt. We like it to end happily, Mama."

"Very well. Listen quietly now. Don't rustle your wings nor flop your tails. Sammy! stop blowing flames into your sister's face, this moment! — or not a word shall you hear.

"There was once a most delightful land, full of bogs

13

and moist-smelling marshes, of dark rocky caves, all damp and cold. The lakes were covered with beautiful green mold, no flowers grew in the fields — nothing but cool rushes, ferns, and mosses. In short, it was a land in which any dragon might be glad to crawl: no sunshine to shrink the scales or dry the wings, no bright glaring meadows to dazzle one's poor eyes. Why, even at midday one could slide comfortably about on the slippery, slimy banks and never catch a blink of a sunbeam on the water."

"Oh, how nice! Really and truly, Mama?" asked the small dragons, laughing with so much delight that the flames from their pretty scarlet throats lighted up the cave until Mr. Dragon stirred uneasily in his dreams; for he had fallen asleep.

"Really and truly," their mother went on, in a lower tone. "In this charming country, your father and I began our cave-keeping. We were very happy for a time, for not too far from us was your father's estate — a fertile valley well stocked with plump and well-flavored inhabitants. You have never seen any whole men, have you?"

"No," they replied eagerly. "What are they like?"

"Oh, so ugly. To begin with, they have no scales, no wings, no claws — "

"No wings and no claws? How frightful they must be!" exclaimed young Samuel Dragon, Jr., proudly expanding his green pinions.

"Not a wing!" replied Mrs. Dragon. "And they walk, when mature, exclusively on their hind legs."

"Why is that?" asked the children.

"I cannot tell. It does seem absurd. When young

they go on all-fours like sensible animals; but the elders pull and persuade, teach and coax, until the poor little things rear up on their hind legs, and then the foolish old ones seem satisfied. Men are very queer. When they first came on this earth,— this earth where dragons dwell, — they lived, properly enough, in caves like the rest of the world. But they are a stupid and restless kind of creatures, and soon began to tear pieces out of the world to make caves to suit themselves. Now they slaughter trees, slice and split them, fasten the pieces together, and stalk in and out of queer little holes called ' doors.' But I cannot spare time to tell you any more about their curious instincts — you must read it for yourselves some day in the ' Dragon's Economical Cave-keeper,' the marketing manual. Look in the index under ' Animal Foods : Apes, Men, and various Bipeds.' You will find it interesting — and useful too.

"As I said, we were happy for a time. We used to stroll out quietly in the evening, and often managed to secure a nice chubby man or two in an hour's flight. But at length came an age when those mean creatures decided to revolt. That is, they kept in their little caves at night, and compelled us to go out so frequently in the unhealthful, glaring daylight, that our scales were hardly fit to be seen. Even with all this exposure, we would succeed in catching only some of the little ones : indeed, during a whole month I caught nothing but two thin miserable specimens. Think how your poor mother suffered ! I was almost starved. I became so thin that I rattled ! "

Mrs. Dragon looked at the young audience, and saw

that the eyes of the two smallest were really shedding sparks. She was touched by their sympathy, but, fearing the story was becoming too sad, hastened to brighten it.

"Well, dears, it did not last long. Your father was young, rash, and brave, in those nights. One dawn he said, 'Really, Scalena, this will not do. I can stand this foolishness no longer!' I asked what he intended; but he waved his tail in a threatening way, and smiled knowingly as he whetted his claws on a new piece of sandstone. The next night, bidding me not to be anxious, he left me. I looked after him as long as I could see the flames in the sky, and then returned wearily to our cave to pick the last bone.

"The next morning, just at dawn, he returned with a delicious marketing,— he said it was a *butcher*, I think, though it may have been a *judge;* the flavor is much the same. Then, when we had retired into the darkest, dampest, coziest corner of the cave, he told me very modestly the story of his great achievement.

"Your brave father, children, had been down to where the whole swarm of men lived, and actually had beaten to pieces one of the wooden caves! He made light of his exploit, and only rejoiced in it because, as he said, he had no fear now of famine or even of scarcity. We sat up late that happy morning, enjoyed a delicious supper, and slept soundly until nightfall.

"We arose with the moon; and after a hasty but effective toilet on his new sandstone, your father advanced glidingly toward the mouth of the cave, when suddenly there presented itself a dark object with a shiny coat, much like that of a dragon. Indeed, we thought for a moment it was some neighbor who had dropped in to breakfast. But in a few seconds we saw that it was what is called a *knight*. A knight, children, is an animal which, although edible, is noxious, and sometimes dangerous to young or careless dragons. I have heard of such being even killed by this spiteful little pest. They are found among men — in fact, they are a species of men that has a hard shell. You know there are hard-shell crabs and soft-shell crabs, and so, likewise, there are hard- and soft-shelled men. Our visitor was a hard-shell who had, while prowling about, found our cave either by accident or wilfully.

" I do not deny that I was a trifle anxious, but your father was merely angry. Giving a great roar, he blew out a mass of dark smoke and scarlet flames at the unfortunate little knight.

" But, though small, the knight was plucky and showed fight. As your father carelessly leaped toward him, the knight scratched dear Papa slightly with a long, hard stick, on the end of which was a bit of very hard shell. Then the knight rode out — for he had enslaved an unfortunate horse, as these cruel men do, my pets, and by means of a contrivance in its mouth, he made it carry him about wherever he chose.

" Your father eagerly followed, though I sought in vain to restrain him. ' No, Scalena,' said he. ' This is a question of principle ! As a true dragon and your loving mate, it is my duty to destroy this dangerous little fellow. Do not be foolish ; I will bring you the body of the fierce creature. They are excellent eating. But you must sharpen your claws, my dear, for the shells are exceedingly hard to remove and most difficult of digestion.

"I obeyed him, for your father is always right, and out he flew with a rush of smoke and flame."

"Oh, Mother!— and was Father killed?" asked one of the youngest — little Tommy Dragon.

"Of course not!" replied his elder brother scornfully. "Don't you see him sleeping over there, all safe and sound? Don't be so silly!"

"You must not speak so sharply to your little brother," said Mrs. Dragon, "or I shall end the story at once!"

"Oh, please go on," exclaimed all the young dragons; "it is just the most interesting part!"

Pleased with their eagerness, she resumed: —

"I did not see the hunt, but your father has often described it to me. The knight came wickedly at him, hoping to scratch him with the sharp stick; but with one whisk of his long green tail, your father broke the thing into small pieces! So you see, Sam," said this thoughtful parent, turning slyly to her eldest son, "it is most important to practise your tail-whisking — and I hope you will not forget it when you go to your next lesson."

Sammy Dragon turned saffron with confusion, but it was evident that he resolved to profit by the little moral so ingeniously woven, by careful Mrs. Dragon, into a mere man-story.

"After the stick was broken," she went on, "the vicious little knight snatched out another, made entirely of the hard shell with which the first was only tipped. With this he tried his worst to break some of your father's lovely scales. Think what a ferocious animal this knight must have been! I cannot see what they are made for. But, then, it is instinct, perhaps; we must not judge him too harshly.

"This new weapon met the fate of the other. It was crunched up by your father's strong teeth, and then he descended upon the little hard-shell man with a great swoop — and that decided the battle! Your father is a modest dragon, but he was really proud of the swiftness with which he ended that conflict. After he once had a fair opportunity to use his newly sharpened claws, there was no doubt of the result!

"We ate the knight at our next meal. I was glad to welcome your father; but he said, 'Pooh! nonsense!' and made light of the whole matter!'"

The young dragons were delighted, and even thought of asking for another story; but their mother, for the first time, noticed that it was almost broad daylight.

"But goodness, children, I hear the horrid little birds singing!" said she. "Run away to bed with you. Wrap yourselves up tight in your moist wings, and be sure to sleep on damp rocks in a draught where you will keep good and cold."

The youngsters crawled away to rest, while Mrs. Dragon went to rouse the Honorable Samuel P. Dragon. To her surprise she saw his great green eyes glowing with a sulphurous satisfaction.

"There are no times like the old times!" said he, drowsily. "That was really a splendid hunt!"

"Yes, dear," replied his mate, with a proud and happy smile; "but I had no idea *you* were listening to my foolish stories. We must now go to rest, or you won t be up till midnight — and then there won't be a single man about. Remember, 'It is the late dragon that catches the knight.'"

The Honorable Samuel P. Dragon rubbed his claws gently together as he selected a nice cozy place for the day. He was humming to himself, and faithful Mrs. Dragon smiled fondly as she recognized the tune. It was:

"I fear no foe in shining armor!"

"Ah!" said she to herself, "the old people like man-stories as well as the little ones!"

PRECOCIOUS PIGGY

By THOMAS HOOD.

PIGGY GOES OUT TO SEE THE WORLD.

WHERE are you going to, you little
    pig?
"I'm leaving my Mother, I'm
    growing so big!"
      So big, young pig,
      So young, so big!
What, leaving your Mother,
    you foolish young pig?

[Illustrated by Tom Hood the Younger.]

21

PIGGY TAKES TO LANDSCAPE GARDENING.

W HERE are you going to, you little
 pig?
 "I've got a new spade, and I'm
 going to dig!"
 To dig, little pig!
 A little pig dig!
Well, I never saw a pig with a spade that
 could dig!

PIGGY GOES OUT DRIVING.

WHERE are you going to, you
    little pig?
  "Why, I'm going to have a nice
    ride in a gig!"
      In a gig, little pig!
        What, a pig in a gig!
Well, I never yet saw a pig ride in
    a gig!

PIGGY TAKES TO DRINKING.

W HERE are you going to, you little
   pig?
   "Well, I'm going to the Queen's Head
   to have a nice swig!"
      A swig, little pig!
      A pig have a swig!
   What, a pig at the Queen's Head having a swig!

PIGGY GOES TO A GRAND BALL.

WHERE are you going to, you little
pig?
"Why, I'm going to the Ball to
dance a fine jig!"
A jig, little pig!
A pig dance a jig!
Well, I never before saw a pig
dance a jig!

PIGGY GOES TO THE FAIR.

WHERE are you going to, you
little pig?
"I'm going to the fair to run
a fine rig!"
A rig, little pig!
A pig run a rig!
Well, I never before saw a pig run
a rig!

PIGGY GOES FOR A WIG.

WHERE are you going to, you little
pig?
"I'm going to the Barber's to buy
me a wig!"
A wig, little pig!
A pig in a wig!
Why, whoever before saw a pig in a wig!

PIGGY BEWAILS HIS APPROACHING FATE.

WHERE are you going to, you
    little pig?
"The Butcher is coming,
    I've grown so big!"
      The Butcher! Poor
        pig!
      Are you grown so
        big?
Well, I think it high time,
    then, you hop the twig!

THE CHESHIRE CAT AND THE LOBSTER QUADRILLE

(FROM ALICE'S ADVENTURES IN WONDERLAND.)

By LEWIS CARROLL.

OR a minute or two Alice stood looking at the house, and wondering what to do next, when suddenly a footman in livery came running out of the wood (she considered him to be a footman because he was in livery: otherwise, judging by his face only, she would have called him a fish) and rapped loudly at the door with his knuckles. It was opened by another footman in livery, with a round face and large eyes like a frog; and both footmen, Alice noticed, had powdered hair that curled all over their heads. She felt very curious to know what it was all about, and crept a little way out of the wood to listen.

The Fish-Footman began by producing from under his arm a great letter, nearly as large as himself, and this he handed over to the other, saying in a solemn tone, "For the Duchess. An invitation from the Queen to play croquet." The Frog-Footman repeated in the same solemn tone, only changing the order of the words a little, "From the Queen. An invitation for the Duchess to play croquet."

Then they both bowed low, and their curls got entangled together.

Alice laughed so much at this that she had to run back into the wood for fear of their hearing her, and when she next peeped out the Fish-Footman was gone, and the other was sitting on the ground near the door, staring stupidly up into the sky.

Alice went timidly up to the door, and knocked.

"There's no sort of use in knocking," said the Footman, "and that for two reasons. First, because I'm on the same side of the door as you are ; secondly, because they're making such a noise inside, no one could possibly hear you." And certainly there *was* a most extraordinary noise going on within — a constant howling and sneezing, and every now and then a great crash, as if a dish or kettle had been broken to pieces.

"Please, then," said Alice, "how am I to get in ?"

"There might be some sense in your knocking," the Footman went on without attending to her, "if we had the door between us. For instance, if you were *inside*, you might knock, and I could let you out, you know." He was looking up into the sky all the time he was speaking, and this Alice thought decidedly uncivil. "But perhaps he can't help it," she said to herself ; "his eyes are so *very* nearly at the top of his head. But at any rate he might answer questions — How am I to get in ?" she repeated, aloud.

"I shall sit here," the Footman remarked, "till to-morrow ——"

At this moment the door of the house opened, and a large plate came skimming out, straight at the Footman's head: it just grazed his nose, and broke to pieces against one of the trees behind him.

"—— or next day, maybe," the Footman continued in the same tone, exactly as if nothing had happened.

"How am I to get in?" Alice asked again in a louder tone.

"*Are* you to get in at all?" said the Footman. "That's the first question, you know."

It was, no doubt: only Alice did not like to be told so. "It's really dreadful," she muttered to herself, "the way all the creatures argue. It's enough to drive one crazy!"

The Footman seemed to think this a good opportunity for repeating his remark with variations. "I shall sit here," he said, "on and off, for days and days."

"But what am *I* to do?" said Alice.

"Anything you like," said the Footman, and began whistling.

"Oh, there's no use in talking to him," said Alice desperately; "he's perfectly idiotic!"   And she opened the door and went in.   The door led right into a large kitchen, which was full of smoke from one end to the other: the Duchess was sitting on a three-legged stool in the middle, nursing a baby; the cook was leaning over the fire, stirring a large caldron which seemed to be full of soup.

"There's certainly too much pepper in that soup!" Alice said to herself, as well as she could for sneezing.

There was certainly too much of it in the air.   Even the Duchess sneezed occasionally; and as for the baby, it was sneezing and howling alternately without a moment's pause. The only two creatures in the kitchen that did not sneeze were the cook, and a large cat which was sitting on the hearth and grinning from ear to ear.

"Please, would you tell me," said Alice, a little timidly, for she was not quite sure whether it was good manners for her to speak first, "why your cat grins like that?"

"It's a Cheshire cat," said the Duchess, "and that's why. Pig!"

She said the last word with such sudden violence that Alice quite jumped; but she saw in another moment that it was addressed to the baby, and not to her, so she took courage, and went on again:

"I didn't know that Cheshire cats always grinned; in fact, I didn't know that cats *could* grin."

"They all can," said the Duchess; "and most of 'em do."

"I don't know of any that do," Alice said very politely, feeling quite pleased to have got into a conversation.

"You don't know much," said the Duchess; "and that's a fact."

Alice did not at all like the tone of this remark, and thought it would be as well to introduce some other subject of conversation. While she was trying to fix on one, the cook took the caldron of soup off the fire, and at once set to work throwing everything within her reach at the Duchess and the baby — the fire-irons came first ; then followed a shower of saucepans, plates and dishes. The Duchess took no notice of them, even when they hit her ; and the baby was howling so much already, that it was quite impossible to say whether the blows hurt it or not.

" Oh, *please* mind what you are doing ! " cried Alice, jumping up and down in an agony of terror. " Oh, there goes his *precious* nose ! " as an unusually large saucepan flew close by it, and very nearly carried it off.

" If everybody minded their own business," said the Duchess in a hoarse growl, " the world would go round a deal faster than it does."

" Which would *not* be an advantage," said Alice, who felt very glad to get an opportunity of showing off a little of her knowledge. " Just think what work it would make with the day and night ! You see the earth takes twenty-four hours to turn round on its axis —— "

" Talking of axes," said the Duchess, " chop off her head ! "

Alice glanced rather anxiously at the cook, to see if she meant to take the hint ; but the cook was busily stirring the soup, and seemed not to be listening, so she went on again : " Twenty-four hours, I *think ;* or is it twelve ? I —— "

" Oh, don't bother *me*," said the Duchess ; " I never

could abide figures." And with that she began nursing her child again, singing a sort of lullaby to it as she did so, and giving it a violent shake at the end of every line :

> " Speak roughly to your little boy,
> 　　And beat him when he sneezes ;
> 　He only does it to annoy,
> 　　Because he knows it teases."

CHORUS.

(in which the cook and the baby joined);

" Wow ! wow ! wow !"

While the Duchess sang the second verse of the song, she kept tossing the baby violently up and down, and the poor little thing howled so, that Alice could hardly hear the words :

> " I speak severely to my boy,
> 　I beat him when he sneezes ;
> For he can thoroughly enjoy
> 　The pepper when he pleases !"

CHORUS.

" Wow ! wow ! wow !"

" Here ! you may nurse it a bit, if you like !" said the Duchess to Alice, flinging the baby at her as she spoke. " I must go and get ready to play croquet with the Queen," and she hurried out of the room. The cook threw a fryingpan after her as she went, but it just missed her.

Alice caught the baby with some difficulty, as it was a queer-shaped little creature, and held out its arms and legs in all directions, " just like a starfish," thought

Alice.   The poor little thing was snorting like a steam engine when she caught it, and kept doubling itself up and straightening itself out again, so that altogether, for the first minute or two, it was as much as she could do to hold it.

As soon as she had made out the proper way of nursing it (which was to twist it up into a sort of knot, and then keep tight hold of its right ear and left foot, so as to prevent its undoing itself), she carried it out into the open air.   "If I don't take this child away with me," thought Alice, "they're sure to kill it in a day or two: wouldn't it be murder to leave it behind?" She said the last words out loud, and the little thing grunted in reply (it had left off sneezing by this time).   "Don't grunt," said Alice: "that's not at all a proper way of expressing yourself."

The baby grunted again, and Alice looked very anxiously into its face to see what was the matter with it.   There could be no doubt that it had a *very* turn-up nose, much more like a snout than a real nose; also its eyes were getting extremely small, for a baby: altogether Alice did not like the look of the thing at all.   "But perhaps it was only sobbing," she thought, and looked into its eyes again, to see if there were any tears.

No, there were no tears.   "If you're going to turn into a pig, my dear," said Alice, seriously, "I'll have nothing more to do with you.   Mind now!"   The poor little thing sobbed again (or grunted, it was impossible to say which), and they went on for some while in silence.

Alice was just beginning to think to herself, "Now, what am I to do with this creature when I get it home?" when it grunted again, so violently, that she looked down into its face in some alarm. This time there could be *no* mistake about it: it was neither more nor less than a pig, and she felt that it would be quite absurd for her to carry it any further.

So she set the little creature down, and felt quite relieved to see it trot away quietly into the wood. "If it had grown up," she said to herself, "it would have been a dreadfully ugly child: but it makes rather a handsome pig, I think." And she began thinking over other children she knew, who might do very well as pigs, and was just saying to herself, "If one only knew the right way to change them —— " when she was a little startled by seeing the Cheshire Cat sitting on a bough of a tree a few yards off.

The Cat only grinned when it saw Alice. It looked

good-natured, she thought; still it had *very* long claws and a great many teeth, so she felt it ought to be treated with respect.

"Cheshire Puss," she began, rather timidly, as she did not at all know whether it would like the name: however, it only grinned a little wider. "Come, it's pleased so far," thought Alice, and she went on, "Would you tell me, please, which way I ought to walk from here?"

"That depends a good deal on where you want to get to," said the Cat.

"I don't much care where —— " said Alice.

"Then it doesn't matter which way you walk," said the Cat.

" —— so long as I get *somewhere*," Alice added as an explanation.

"Oh, you're sure to do that," said the Cat, "if you only walk long enough."

Alice felt that this could not be denied, so she tried another question. "What sort of people live about here?"

"In *that* direction," the Cat said, waving his right paw round, "lives a Hatter; and in *that* direction," waving the other paw, "lives a March Hare. Visit either you like; they're both mad."

"But I don't want to go among mad people," Alice remarked.

"Oh, you can't help that," said the Cat; "we're all mad here. I'm mad. You're mad."

"How do you know I'm mad?" said Alice.

"You must be," said the Cat, "or you wouldn't have come here."

Alice didn't think that proved it at all; however, she went on; "and how do you know that you're mad?"

"To begin with," said the Cat, "a dog's not mad. You grant that?"

"I suppose so," said Alice.

"Well then," the Cat went on, "you see a dog growls when it's angry, and wags its tail when it's pleased. Now *I* growl when I'm pleased, and wag my tail when I'm angry. Therefore I'm mad."

"*I* call it purring, not growling," said Alice.

"Call it what you like," said the Cat. "Do you play croquet with the Queen to-day?"

"I should like it very much," said Alice, "but I haven't been invited yet."

"You'll see me there," said the Cat, and vanished.

Alice was not much surprised at this, she was getting so well used to queer things happening. While she was still looking at the place where it had been, it suddenly appeared again.

"By-the-by, what became of the baby?" said the Cat. "I'd nearly forgotten to ask."

"It turned into a pig," Alice answered very quietly, just as if the Cat had come back in a natural way.

"I thought it would," said the Cat, and vanished again.

Alice waited a little, half expecting to see it again, but it did not appear, and after a minute or two she walked on in the direction in which the March Hare was said to live. "I've seen Hatters before," she said to herself; "the March Hare will be much the most interesting, and perhaps as this is May it won't be

raving mad — at least not so mad as it was in March."
As she said this, she looked up, and there was the Cat
again, sitting on a branch of a tree.

"Did you say pig, or fig?" said the Cat.

"I said pig," re-
plied Alice; "and
I wish you wouldn't
keep appearing and
vanishing so suddenly;
you make one quite
giddy."

"All right," said the
Cat; and this time it vanished quite slowly, begin-
ning with the end of the tail, and ending with the grin,
which remained some time after the rest of it had gone.

"Well, I've often seen a cat without a grin," thought
Alice; "but a grin without a cat! it's the most curious
thing I ever saw in all my life!"

She had not gone much farther before she came in
sight of the house of the March Hare: she thought it
must be the right house, because the chimneys were
shaped like ears and the roof was thatched with fur.
It was so large a house, that she did not like to go
nearer till she had nibbled some more of the left-hand
bit of mushroom, and raised herself to about two feet
high: even then she walked up toward it rather timidly,
saying to herself, "Suppose it should be raving mad after
all; I almost wish I'd gone to see the Hatter instead."

.   .   .   .

The Mock Turtle sighed deeply, and drew the back
of one flapper across his eyes. He looked at Alice and

tried to speak, but for a minute or two sobs choked his voice. " Same as if he had a bone in his throat," said the Gryphon, and it set to work shaking him and punching him in the back. At last the Mock Turtle recovered his voice, and, with tears running down his cheeks, he went on again :

" You may not have lived much under the sea " — (" I haven't," said Alice) — " and perhaps you were never even introduced to a Lobster " — (Alice began to say " I once tasted " — but checked herself hastily, and said, " No, never ") — " so you can have no idea what a delightful thing a Lobster Quadrille is ! "

" No, indeed," said Alice. " What sort of a dance is it?"

" Why," said the Gryphon, " you first form into a line along the seashore —— "

" Two lines ! " cried the Mock Turtle. " Seals, turtles, salmon, and so on : then, when you've cleared all the jelly-fish out of the way —— "

" *That* generally takes some time," interrupted the Gryphon.

" You advance twice —— "

" Each with a lobster as a partner ! " cried the Gryphon.

" Of course," the Mock Turtle said : " advance twice, set to partners —— "

" Change lobsters, and retire in same order," continued the Gryphon.

" Then, you know," the Mock Turtle went on, " you throw the —— "

" The lobsters ! " shouted the Gryphon, with a bound into the air.

" As far out to sea as you can —— "

" Swim after them!" screamed the Gryphon.

"Turn a somersault in the sea!" cried the Mock Turtle, capering wildly about.

" Change lobsters again!" yelled the Gryphon at the top of its voice.

" Back to land again, and — that's all the first figure," said the Mock Turtle, suddenly dropping his voice, and the two creatures, who had been jumping about like mad things all this time, sat down again very sadly and quietly, and looked at Alice.

" It must be a very pretty dance," said Alice timidly.

" Would you like to see a little of it?" said the Mock Turtle.

" Very much indeed," said Alice.

"Come let's try the first figure!" said the Mock Turtle to the Gryphon. " We can do it without lobsters, you know. Which shall sing?"

" Oh, *you* sing," said the Gryphon. " I've forgotten the words."

So they began solemnly dancing round and round Alice, every now and then treading on her toes when they passed too close, and waving their forepaws to mark the time, while the Mock Turtle sang this, very slowly and sadly :

" ' Will you walk a little faster!' said a whiting to a snail,
' There's a porpoise close behind us, and he's treading on my tail.
See how eagerly the lobsters and the turtles all advance!
They are waiting on the shingle — will you come and join the
    dance ?
Will you, won't you, will you, won't you, will you join the
    dance ?
Will you, won't you, will you, won't you, won't you join the
    dance ?

" ' You can really have no notion how delightful it will be
When they take us up and throw us, with the lobsters, out to
    sea ! '
But the snail replied, 'Too far, too far ! ' and gave a look
    askance —
Said he thanked the whiting kindly, but he would not join the
    dance.
Would not, could not, would not, could not, would not join the
    dance.
Would not, could not, would not, could not, could not join the
    dance.

" ' What matters it how far we go ? ' his scaly friend replied,
' There is another shore, you know, upon the other side.
The further off from England the nearer is to France ;
Then turn not pale, beloved snail, but come and join the dance.
Will you, won't you, will you, won't you, will you join the
    dance ?
Will you, won't you, will you, won't you, won't you join the
    dance ? ' "

" Thank you, it's a very interesting dance to watch,"
said Alice, feeling very glad that it was over at last;
" and I do so like that curious song about the whiting ! "

" Oh, as to the whiting," said the Mock Turtle,
" they — you've seen them, of course ? "

" Yes," said Alice, " I've often seen them at
dinn——" she checked herself hastily.

" I don't know where Dinn may be," said the Mock
Turtle, " but if you've seen them so often, of course
you know what they're like."

" I believe so," Alice replied thoughtfully. " They
have their tails in their mouths; and they're all over
crumbs."

" You're wrong about the crumbs," said the Mock
Turtle : " crumbs would all wash off in the sea. But

they *have* their tails in their mouths; and the reason is " — here the Mock Turtle yawned and shut his eyes — " Tell her about the reason and all that," he said to the Gryphon.

" The reason is," said the Gryphon, " that they *would* go with the lobsters to the dance. So they got thrown out to sea. So they had to fall a long way. So they got their tails fast in their mouths. So they couldn't get them out again. That's all."

" Thank you," said Alice. " It's very interesting. I never knew so much about a whiting before."

" I can tell you more than that, if you like," said the Gryphon. "Do you know why it's called a whiting?"

" I never thought about it," said Alice. " Why?"

" *It does the boots and shoes*," the Gryphon replied very solemnly.

Alice was thoroughly puzzled. " Does the boots and shoes!" she repeated in a wondering tone.

" Why, what are *your* shoes done with?" said the Gryphon. " I mean, what makes them so shiny?"

Alice looked down at them, and considered a little before she gave her answer. " They're done with blacking, I believe."

" Boots and shoes under the sea," the Gryphon went on in a deep voice, " are done with whiting. Now you know."

" And what are they made of?" asked Alice in a tone of great curiosity.

"Soles and eels, of course," the Gryphon replied rather impatiently: " any shrimp could have told you that."

" If I'd been the whiting," said Alice, whose thoughts were still running on the song, " I'd have said to the porpoise, 'Keep back, please: we don't want *you* with us!'"

"They were obliged to have him with them," the Mock Turtle said: "no wise fish would go anywhere without a porpoise."

"Wouldn't it really?" said Alice in a tone of great surprise.

"Of course not," said the Mock Turtle; "why, if a fish came to *me*, and told me he was going a journey, I should say, 'With what porpoise?'"

"Don't you mean 'purpose'?" said Alice.

"I mean what I say," the Mock Turtle replied in an offended tone. And the Gryphon added, "Come, let's hear some of *your* adventures."

"I could tell you my adventures — beginning from this morning," said Alice a little timidly; "but it's no use going back to yesterday, because I was a different person then."

"Explain all that," said the Mock Turtle.

"No, no! the adventures first," said the Gryphon in an impatient tone: "explanations take such a dreadful time."

So Alice began telling them her adventures from the time when she first saw the White Rabbit; she was a little nervous about it just at first, the two creatures got so close to her, one on each side, and opened their eyes and mouths so *very* wide, but she gained courage as she went on. Her listeners were perfectly quiet till she got to the part about her repeating "*You are old, Father William,*" to the Caterpillar, and the words all coming different, and then the Mock Turtle drew a long breath, and said, "that's very curious."

"'FOR THE DUCHESS. AN INVITATION FROM THE
QUEEN TO PLAY CROQUET.'"

"It's all about as curious as it can be," said the Gryphon.

"It all .came different!" the Mock Turtle repeated thoughtfully. "I should like to hear her try and repeat something now. Tell her to begin." He looked at the Gryphon as if he thought it had some kind of authority over Alice.

"Stand up and repeat '*'Tis the voice of the slug-gard,*'" said the Gryphon.

"How the creatures order one about, and make one repeat lessons!" thought Alice.

"I might just as well be at school at once." However, she got up, and began to repeat it, but her head was so full of the Lobster Quadrille, that she hardly knew what she was saying, and the words came very queer indeed:

"'Tis the voice of the lobster; I heard him declare,
'You have baked me too brown, I must sugar my hair.'
As a duck with its eyelids, so he with his nose
Trims his belt and his buttons, and turns out his toes."

"That's different from what *I* used to say when I was a child," said the Gryphon.

"Well, I never heard it before," said the Mock Turtle; "but it sounds uncommon nonsense."

Alice said nothing; she had sat down again with her face in her hands, wondering if anything would *ever* happen in a natural way again.

"I should like to have it explained," said the Mock Turtle.

"She can't explain it," said the Gryphon hastily. "Go on with the next verse."

"But about his toes?" the Mock Turtle persisted.

"How *could* he turn them out with his nose, you know?"

"It's the first position in dancing," Alice said; but she was dreadfully puzzled by the whole thing, and longed to change the subject.

"Go on with the next verse," the Gryphon repeated impatiently; "it begins '*I passed by his garden.*'"

Alice did not dare to disobey, though she felt sure it would all come wrong, and she went on in a trembling voice:

"I passed by his garden, and marked
　　with one eye,
　How the owl and the oyster were
　　sharing the pie."

"What *is* the use of repeating all that stuff," the Mock Turtle interrupted, "if you don't explain as you go on? It's by far the most confusing thing *I* ever heard."

"Yes, I think you'd better leave off," said the Gryphon, and Alice was only too glad to do so.

"Shall we try another figure of the Lobster Quadrille?" the Gryphon went on. "Or would you like the Mock Turtle to sing you a song?"

"Oh, a song, please, if the Mock Turtle would be so kind," Alice replied, so eagerly that the Gryphon said, in a rather offended tone, "Hm! No accounting for tastes! Sing her '*Turtle soup*' will you, old fellow?"

The Mock Turtle sighed deeply, and began, in a voice sometimes choked with sobs, to sing this:

"Beautiful Soup, so rich and green,
Waiting in a hot tureen!
Who for such dainties would not stoop?
Soup of the evening, beautiful Soup!
Soup of the evening, beautiful Soup!
    Beau—ootiful Soo—oop!
    Beau—ootiful Soo—oop!
Soo—oop of the e—e—evening,
    Beautiful, beautiful Soup!

"Beautiful Soup! Who cares for fish,
Game, or any other dish?
Who would not give all else for two p
ennyworth only of beautiful Soup?
Pennyworth only of beautiful Soup?
    Beau—ootiful Soup!
    Beau—ootiful Soup!
Soo—oop of the e—e—evening,
    Beautiful, beauti—FUL SOUP!"

"Chorus again," cried the Gryphon, and the Mock Turtle had just begun to repeat it, when a cry of "The trial's beginning," was heard in the distance.

"Come on," cried the Gryphon, and, taking Alice by the hand, it hurried off, without waiting for the end of the song.

"What trial is it?" Alice panted, as she ran, but the Gryphon only answered, "Come on," and ran the faster, while more and more faintly came, carried on the breeze that followed them, the melancholy words:

"Soo—oop of the e—e—evening,
Beautiful, beautiful Soup!"

VERSES FROM LILLIPUT LEVEE

By W. B. Rand.

LILLIPUT LEVEE.

WHERE does Pinafore Palace stand?
  Right in the middle of Lilliput-land!
  There the Queen eats bread-and-honey,
  There the King counts up his money!

Oh, the Glorious Revolution!
Oh, the Provisional Constitution!
Now that the children, clever bold folks,
  Have turned the tables upon the Old Folks!

Easily the thing was done,
For the children were more than two to one;
Brave as lions, quick as foxes,
With hoards of wealth in their money-boxes!

They seized the keys, they patrolled the street,
They drove the policeman off his beat,
They built barricades, they stationed sentries —
You must give the word, when you come to the
    entries!

They dressed themselves in the Riflemen's clothes,
They had pea-shooters, they had arrows and bows,

So as to put resistance down —
Order reigns in Lilliput-town!

They made the baker bake hot rolls,
They made the wharfinger send in coals,
They made the butcher kill the calf,
They cut the telegraph-wires in half.

They went to the chemist's, and with their feet
They kicked the physic all down the street;
They went to the schoolroom and tore the books,
They munched the puffs at the pastrycook's.

They sucked the jam, they lost the spoons,
They sent up several fire-balloons,
They let off crackers, they burnt a guy,
They piled a bonfire ever so high.

They offered a prize for the laziest boy,
And one for the most magnificent toy;
They split or burnt the canes offhand,
They made new laws in Lilliput-land.

Never do to-day what you can
Put off till to-morrow, one of them ran;
Late to bed and late to rise
Was another law which they did devise.

They passed a law to have always plenty
Of beautiful things: we shall mention twenty:
A magic lantern for all to see,
Rabbits to keep, and a Christmas-tree,

A boat, a house that went on wheels,
An organ to grind, and sherry at meals,
Drums and wheelbarrows, Roman candles,
Whips with whistles let into the handles,

A real live giant, a roc to fly,
A goat to tease, a copper to sky,
A garret of apples, a box of paints,
A saw and a hammer, and no complaints.

Nail up the door, slide down the stairs,
Saw off the legs of the parlor chairs —
That was the way in Lilliput-land,
The children having the upper hand.

They made the Old Folks come to school,
And in pinafores, — that was the rule, —
Saying, *Eener-deener-diner-duss,*
Kattler-wheeler-whiler-wuss ;

They made them learn all sorts of things
That nobody liked.   They had catechisings;
They kept them in, they sent them down
In class, in school, in Lilliput-town.

O but they gave them tit-for-tat !
Thick bread-and-butter, and all that ;
Stick-jaw pudding that tires your chin,
With the marmalade spread ever so thin.

They governed the clock in Lilliput-land,
They altered the hour or the minute-hand,

They made the day fast, they made the day slow,
Just as they wished the time to go.

They never waited for king or for cat;
They never wiped their shoes on the mat;
Their joy was great; their joy was greater;
They rode in the baby's perambulator!

There was a Levee in Lilliput-town,
At Pinafore Palace.   Smith and Brown,
Jones and Robinson had to attend —
All to whom they cards did send.

Every one rode in a cab to the door;
Every one came in a pinafore;
Lady and gentleman, rat-tat-tat,
Loud knock, proud knock, opera hat!

The place was covered with silver and gold,
The place was as full as it ever could hold;
The ladies kissed her Majesty's hand,
Such was the custom in Lilliput-land.

His Majesty knighted eight or ten,
Perhaps a score, of the gentlemen,
Some of them short and some of them tall —
Arise, Sir What's-a-name What-do-you-call!

Nuts and nutmeg (that's in the negus);
The bill of fare would perhaps fatigue us;
Forty-five fiddlers to play the fiddle;
Right foot, left foot, down the middle.

Conjuring tricks with the poker and tongs,
Riddles and forfeits, singing of songs;
One fat man, too fat by far,
Tried " Twinkle, twinkle, little star."

His voice was gruff, his pinafore tight,
His wife said, " Mind, dear, sing it right,"
But he forgot, and said Fa-la-la!
The Queen of Lilliput's own papa!

She frowned, and ordered him up to bed:
He said he was sorry; she shook her head;
His clean shirt-front with his tears was stained —
But discipline had to be maintained.

The Constitution!   The Law!   The Crown!
Order reigns in Lilliput-town!
The Queen is Jill, and the King is John;
I trust the Government will get on.

I noticed, being a man of rhymes,
An advertisement in the *Lilliput Times*: —
" PINAFORE PALACE.   This is to state
That the Court is in want of a Laureate.

" Nothing menial required.
Poets, willing to be hired,
May send in Specimens at once,
Care of the Chamberlain DOUBLEDUNCE."

Said I to myself Here's a chance for me
The Lilliput Laureate for to be!
And these are the Specimens I sent in
To Pinafore Palace.   Shall I win?

PUBLIC NOTICE. — *This is to state
That these are the specimens left at the gate
Of Pinafore Palace, exact to date,
In the hands of the porter, Curlypate,
Who sits in his plush on a chair of state,
By the gentleman who is a candidate
For the office of* LILLIPUT LAUREATE.

THE BEWITCHED TOYS; OR, QUEEN MAB IN CHILD-WORLD.

I

HERE comes Queen Mab in her coach-and-
six!
    Look out for mischievous fairy tricks!
    Look out, good girls! Look out, brave
      boys!
    I know she comes to bewitch your toys!
    Hither she floats, like the down of a
      thistle! —
So mind the peg-top; and mind the hoop;
Bring down the kite with a sudden swoop;
Hide the popgun; and plug up the whistle;
But don't say Dolly's a-bed with the croup:
For, if you tell her a fib, my dear,
She'll fasten the door-key to your ear!

II

Then the Kite went flying up to the Moon.
    And the Man with the Sticks, who lives up there,
Kick'd it through with his clouted shoon,
    And the tail hung dangling down in the air.

But Harry wouldn't let go the string,
    Although it nearly broke with the strain;
Said he: " Well, this is a comical thing,
    But the kite is mine, and I'll have it again!"

"Now whistle three times," cried cunning Nell,
  "And over your shoulder throw your shoe,
And pull once more, and say this spell:
  FUSTUMFUNNIDOSTANTARABOO!"

But Harry made a mistake in the charm,
  Saying, "FUSTUMFUNNIDOSTANTABOORACK!"
And a dreadful pain went all up his arm,
  And he fell down, shouting, right on his back.

Then Nell took hold, and pulled the string,
  And the kite came down, all safe and sound,
And a piece of the moon away did bring,
  Which you may have for a silver pound!

III

Said Thomas, with the round straw hat,
  "My popgun bring to me,
And hey! to shoot the Tabby Cat
  Up in the Cherry-tree!

"Last night she stole my supper all,
  She must be better taught;
And I shall make her caterwaul
  I'm sorry,' as she ought."

Then Thomas, taking hasty aim
  At Tabby on the bough,
Hit Tabby's mistress, an old Dame
  Who had a Brindled Cow.

The Brindled Cow could not abide
　　To see her mistress struck,
And after trembling Thomas hied, —
　　Said he, " It's just my luck ! "

She tossed him once, she tossed him twice,
　　When Tabby at her flew,
Saying, " Tom, your custard was so nice
　　That I will fight for you."

The old Dame flung the pellet back,
　　And, when Tom picked it up,
He cried, " The pellet has turned, good lack !
　　To a custard in a cup ! "

And so it had !　The Brindled Cow,
　　The Dame and Tabby Cat
Were much surprised.　" It's strange, I vow,"
　　Said Tom in the round hat.

But nothing came amiss to him ;
　　He ate the custard clean —
There was a brown mark round the rim
　　To show where it had been.

IV

" Pegtop, pegtop — fast asleep !
Pray, how long do you mean to keep
Humming and droning and spinning away ?
Do you mean to keep on all the day ?
Ten minutes have passed since your nap was begun ;
Pegtop, when will your nap be done ?

" Forty winks, forty, and forty more!
You never slept so long before;
This is a pretty sleep to take!
Boxer, Boxer, yawn and wake!"

Then said Marian, " Never fear;
Dolly's nightcap, Richard dear,
Put on Boxer — perhaps he thinks
He would like forty times forty winks!"

Three o'clock, four o'clock, all day long
Richard's Pegtop hummed so strong,
Hummed away and would not stop —
Dick had to buy another top!
For though this Boxer was certainly clever,
Who wants a Pegtop to hum forever?
All the Queen's horses and all the Queen's men
Couldn't get Boxer to wake again;
They made him a house, and put him in;
The people came to see Boxer spin;
" A penny apiece," said Dick, " and cheap,
To see my pegtop's wonderful sleep!"

V

Kate had quarrelled and would not speak
      To Cousin John,
Who, trying to kiss her on the cheek,
      With her bonnet on,
Had crumpled her bonnet at the border,
And put the trimming in disorder.

"Pray let me kiss you, Katy dear,"
        Said John so gay.
"Now, Master John," said Kate severe,
        "Please get away!
And if you don't, I only hope
You'll get hit with my skipping-rope!"

        Skip, skip,
        Never trip;
        Round and round!
        "Does it touch the ground?
Don't I skip well?" said sulky Kate;
        But, oh, at last
        Her feet stuck fast —
        Her pretty feet,
        So small and neat,
Were glued by magic to the skipping-cord,
Which turned into a Swing!   And then my lord
Johnny said, "This is fine, upon my word!"
Backwards and forwards Katy swung; —
To the magic rope, which by nothing hung,
Frightened out of her breath she clung —
An apple for the Queen, and a pear for the King!
Wasn't that a wonderful swing?
It kept on going like anything!

"John?" said Katy, turning faint,
And the colour of white paint,
"Save me from this dreadful swing!"
Then our Johnny made a spring
Up to Kate, and held her tight,
And kissed her twice, with all his might,

Which stopped the magic swing; and Katy then
Said, "Thank you, Jack!" and kissed him back again.

VI

Then the Children all said, "She spoils our play:
We must really get Queen Mab away;
She mustn't betwitch our Toys too much.
Who will speak to her?   Does she talk Dutch?
John knows Magic, and Greek, and such;
No one than John can be cleverer —
Perhaps he knows how to get rid of her!"

VII

Six White Mice, with harness on,
What do you think of Cousin John,
    Who taught them so,
    And made them go? —
Six white mice, with harness on!

A wee coach, gilt like the Lord Mayor's own!
Made by Cousin John alone,
    Bright and gay, —
    On a Lord Mayor's Day
Just such a coach is the Lord Mayor's own!

Marian's Doll come out for a ride,
Dressed like a queen in pomp and pride:
    The six wee mice,
    That trot so nice,
Draw Marian's Doll come out for a ride!

Every mouse had a silver bell
Round its neck, as I've heard tell;
   Tinkle tink! —
   But who would think
Of a harnessed mouse, with a silver bell?

" What can six white mice intend ? "
Thought Queen Mab, with her hair on end —
   " And silver bells,
   And what-not-else —
What can six white mice intend?

" When was such a procession seen?
It frightens me, as I'm a Queen! "
   So she stopped her tricks,
   And her coach-and-six
Drove away with the Fairy Queen.

HAROLD AND ALICE; OR, THE REFORMED GIANT

I

THE Giant sat on a rock up high,
    With the wind in his shaggy hair;
And he said, " I have drained the dairies
    dry,
    And stripped the orchards bare;

" I have eaten the sheep, with the wool on their backs,"
    (A nasty giant was he,)
" The eggs and the shells, the honey, the wax,
    The fowls, and the cock-turkéy;

" And now I think I could eat a score
    Of babies so plump and small;
And if, after that, I should want any more,
    Their brothers and sisters and all.

" To-morrow I'll do it.   Ha! what was that?"
    Said he, for a sound he heard;
" Was it fluttering owl or pattering rat,
    Or bough to the breeze that stirred!"

Oh, it was neither rat nor owl,
    Giant! nor shaking leaf;
Young Harold has heard your scheme so foul,
    And it may come to grief!

One thing which you ate has escaped your mind, —
    Young Harold his guinea-pig dear;
And he has crept up to try and find
    His pet, and he shakes with fear;

He has hid himself in a corner, you know,
    To listen and look about;
And if to the village to-morrow you go,
    You may find the babes gone out!

II

Now, when to the village came Harold back
    And told his tale so wild,
Then every mother she cried, "Good lack!
    My child! preserve my child!"

And every father took his sword
    And sharpened it on a stone;
But little Harold said never a word,
    Having a plan of his own.

He laid six harrows outside the stile
    That led to the village green,
Then on them a little hay did pile,
    For the prongs not to be seen.

A toothsome sucking-pig he slew,
    And thereby did it lay;
For why? Because young Harold knew
    The Giant would pass that way.

Then he went in and said his prayers, —
    Not to lie down to sleep;
But at his window up the stairs
    A watch all night did keep,

Till the little stars all went pale to bed,
    Because the sun was out,
And the sky in the east grew dapple-red,
    And the little birds chirped about.

III

Now, all the village was early awake,
    And, with short space to pray,
Their preparations they did make,
    To bear the babes away.

The horses were being buckled in, —
    The little ones looked for a ride, —
When on came the Giant, as ugly as Sin,
    With a terrible six-yard stride.

Then every woman and every child
    To scream aloud began;
Young Harold up at his watch-tower smiled,
    And his sword drew every man;

For now the Giant, fierce and big,
    Came near to the stile by the green,
But when he saw that luscious pig
    His lips grew wet between!

Now, left foot, right foot, step it again,
  He trod on —— the harrow spikes!
And how he raged and roared with pain
  He may describe who likes.

At last he fell, and as he lay
  Loud bellowing on the ground,
The stalwart men of the village, they
  With drawn swords danced around.

" O spare my life, I you entreat!
  I will be a Giant good!
O take out those thorns that prick my feet,
  Which now are bathed in blood!"

Then the little village maids did feel
  For this Giant so shaggy-haired,
And to their parents they did kneel,
  Saying, " Let his life be spared!"

His bleeding wounds the maids did bind;
  They framed a litter strong
With all the hurdles they could find;
  Six horses drew him along;

And all the way to his castle rude
  Up high in the piny rocks,
He promised to be a giant good —
  The cruel, crafty fox!

IV.

" O mother, lend me your largest tub!" —
  " Why, daughter! tell me quick!" —

" O mother, to make a syllabub
   For the Giant who is so sick."

Now in fever-fit the Giant lay,
   From the pain in his wounded feet,
And hoping soon would come the day
   When he might the babies eat.

" O mother, dress me in white, I beg,
   With flowers and pretty gear;
For Mary and Madge, and Jess and Peg,
   And all my playmates dear,

" We go to the Giant's this afternoon,
   To carry him something nice, —
A custard three times as big as the moon,
   With sugar and wine and spice."

" O daughter, your father shall go with you;
   Suppose the Giant is well,
And eats you up, what shall we do?"
   Then her thought did Alice tell: —

" No, mother dear; we go alone,
   And Heaven for us will care;
If the Giant bad has a heart of stone,
   We will soften it with prayer!"

Now, when the Giant saw these maids,
   Drest all in white, draw near,
He twitched his monstrous shoulder-blades,
   And dropped an honest tear!

"Dear Giant, a syllabub nice we bring,
    Pray let us tuck you in!"
The Giant said, "Sweet innocent thing!
    Oh, I am a lump of sin!

"Go home, and say to the man of prayer
    To make the church-door wide,
For I next Sunday will be there,
    And kneel, dears, at your side.

"Tell brave young Harold I forgive
    Him for the harrow-spikes;
And I will do, please Heaven I live,
    What penance the prayer-man likes.

"Set down, my dears, the syllabub,
    And as I better feel,
I'll try and eat a fox's cub
    At my next mid-day meal;

"And all my life the village I'll keep
    From harmful vermin free;
But never more will eat up the sheep,
    The honey, or cock-turkéy!"

v

Now Sunday came, and in the aisle
    Did kneel the Giant tall;
The priest could not forbear a smile,
    The church it looked so small!

And, as the Giant walked away,
    He knocked off the roof with his head;
But he quarried stones on the following day,
    To build another instead.

And it was high and broad and long,
    And a hundred years it stood,
To tell of the Giant so cruel and strong
    That kindness had made good.

GODFREY GORDON GUSTAVUS GORE.

ODFREY GORDON GUSTAVUS GORE—
No doubt you have heard the name before —
Was a boy who never would shut a door!

The wind might whistle, the wind might roar,
And teeth be aching and throats be sore,
But still he never would shut the door.

His father would beg, his mother implore,
"Godfrey Gordon Gustavus Gore,
We really *do* wish you would shut the door!"

Their hands they wrung, their hair they tore;
But Godfrey Gordon Gustavus Gore
Was deaf as the buoy out at the Nore.

When he walked forth the folks would roar,
"Godfrey Gordon Gustavus Gore,
Why don't you think to shut the door?"

They rigged out a Shutter with sail and oar,
And threatened to pack off Gustavus Gore
On a voyage of penance to Singapore.

But he begged for mercy, and said, "No more!
Pray do not send me to Singapore
On a Shutter, and then I will shut the door!"

" You will ? " said his parents ; " then keep on shore!
But mind you do !   For the plague is sore
Of a fellow that never will shut the door,
Godfrey Gordon Gustavus Gore ! "

THE ABSENT BOY.

 I KNOW an absent-minded boy,
To meditate is all his joy;
He seldom does the thing he ought
Because he is so rapt in thought.

At marbles he can never win;
He wears his waistcoat outside in;
He cannot add a sum up right;
And often he is not polite.

His mother cries, " My poor heart breaks,
Because the child makes such mistakes;
He never knows," she says with sighs,
" Which side his bread the butter lies!"

One day, absorbed in meditation,
He roamed into a railway station,
And in a corner of a train
Sat down, with inattentive brain.

They rang the bell, the whistle blew,
They shook the flags, the engine flew;
But all the noise did not induce
This boy to quit his mood abstruse.

And when three hours were past and gone
He found himself at Something*ton;*
" What is this place?" he sighed in vain,
For railway men can not speak plain.

When he got home his parents had
To pay his fare, which was too bad;
More than two hundred miles, alas!
The Absent Boy had gone first-class.

For Fear he should, in absentness,
Forget his own name and address
Whilst he pursues his meditations,
And so be lost to his relations,

Would it be best that he should wear
A collar like our Tray? or bear
His name and home in indigo
Pricked on his shoulder, or below?

The chief objection to this plan
Is, that his father is a man
Who often moves.   If we begin
To prick the Boy's home on his skin,

Before long he will be tattooed
With indigo from head to foot:
Perhaps a label on his chest
Would meet the difficulty best.

TIMOTHY TIGHT.

TIMOTHY TIGHT, Timothy Tight,
  Says he will neither have sup nor bite,
  Nor comb his hair, nor sleep in his bed,
Till he has done what he thinks in his head.

What is it poor little Timothy thinks
To do before he eats, or drinks,
Or combs, or sleeps? Why, Timothy Tight
Thinks in his head to turn black into white!

He caught a crow, and he tried with that,
He tried again with a great black cat,
He tried again with dyes and inks ;
He keeps on trying to do what he thinks !

He tried with lumps of coal a score,
He tried with jet, and a blackamoor,
He tried with these till he got vext —
He means to try the Black Sea next.

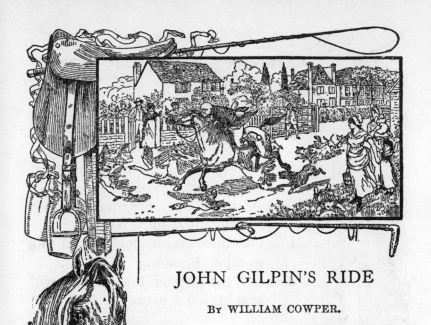

JOHN GILPIN'S RIDE

By WILLIAM COWPER.

JOHN Gilpin was a citizen of
credit and renown;
A train-band captain eke was he,
of famous London town.
John Gilpin's spouse said to her dear,
"Though wedded we have been
These twice ten tedious years, yet we
no holiday have seen.

To-morrow is our wedding-day, and we shall then re-
pair
Unto the bell at Edmonton, all in a chaise-and-pair.
My sister and my sister's child, myself and children
three,
Will fill the chaise: so you must ride on horseback
after we."

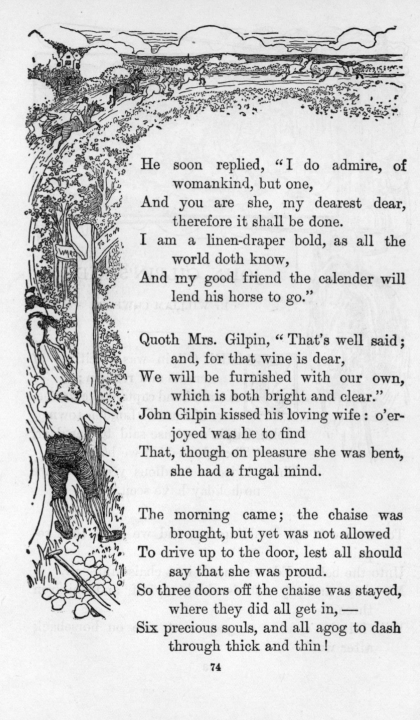

He soon replied, "I do admire, of
    womankind, but one,
And you are she, my dearest dear,
    therefore it shall be done.
I am a linen-draper bold, as all the
    world doth know,
And my good friend the calender will
    lend his horse to go."

Quoth Mrs. Gilpin, "That's well said;
    and, for that wine is dear,
We will be furnished with our own,
    which is both bright and clear."
John Gilpin kissed his loving wife : o'er-
    joyed was he to find
That, though on pleasure she was bent,
    she had a frugal mind.

The morning came; the chaise was
    brought, but yet was not allowed
To drive up to the door, lest all should
    say that she was proud.
So three doors off the chaise was stayed,
    where they did all get in, —
Six precious souls, and all agog to dash
    through thick and thin !

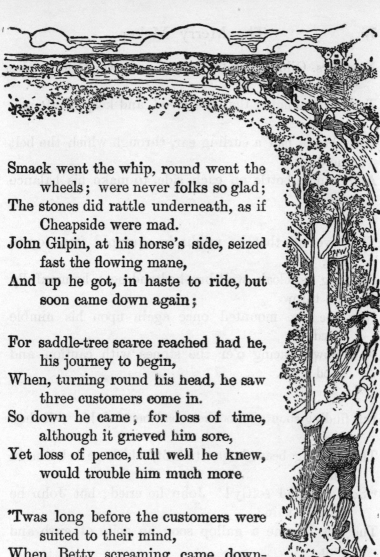

Smack went the whip, round went the
    wheels; were never folks so glad;
The stones did rattle underneath, as if
    Cheapside were mad.
John Gilpin, at his horse's side, seized
    fast the flowing mane,
And up he got, in haste to ride, but
    soon came down again;

For saddle-tree scarce reached had he,
    his journey to begin,
When, turning round his head, he saw
    three customers come in.
So down he came, for loss of time,
    although it grieved him sore,
Yet loss of pence, full well he knew,
    would trouble him much more

'Twas long before the customers were
    suited to their mind,
When Betty screaming came down-
    stairs, "The wine is left behind!"
"Good luck," quoth he; "yet bring it
    me, my leathern belt likewise,
In which I wear my trusty sword
    when I do exercise."

Now Mrs. Gilpin (careful soul!) had two stone bottles
found,
To hold the liquor that she loved, and keep it safe and
sound;
Each bottle had a curling ear, through which the belt
he drew,
And hung a bottle on each side, to make his balance
true.

Then over all, that he might be equipped from top to
toe,
His long red cloak, well brushed and neat, he manfully
did throw.
Now see him mounted once again upon his nimble
steed,
Full slowly pacing o'er the stones with caution and
good heed.

But finding soon a smoother road beneath his well-shod
feet,
The snorting beast began to trot, which galled him in
his seat.
"So! fair and softly!" John he cried; but John he
cried in vain;
The trot became a gallop soon, in spite of curb and
rein.

So, stooping down, as needs he must who cannot sit
upright,
He grasped the mane with both his hands, and eke with
all his might.

His horse, who never in that sort had handled been
before,
What thing upon his back had got did wonder more
and more.

Away went Gilpin, neck or naught; away went hat
and wig;
He little dreamed, when he set out, of running such a
rig.
The wind did blow, the cloak did fly, like streamer long
and gay,
Till, loop and button failing both, at last it flew away.

Then might all people well discern the bottles he had
slung;
A bottle swinging at each side, as hath been said or
sung.
The dogs did bark, the children screamed; up flew the
windows all,
And every soul cried out, " Well done!" as loud as he
could bawl.

Away went Gilpin, who but he! his fame soon spread
around,
" He carries weight!   He rides a race!   'Tis for a
thousand pound!"
And still, as fast as he drew near, 'twas wonderful to
view
How in a trice the turnpike-men their gates wide open
threw.

And now, as he went bowing down his reeking head
full low,

The bottles twain, behind his back, were shattered at a blow.
Down ran the wine into the road, most piteous to be seen,
Which made his horses flanks to smoke, as they had basted been.

But still he seemed to carry weight, with leather girdle braced,
For all might see the bottle-necks still dangling at his waist.
Thus all through merry Islington these gambols he did play,
And till he came unto the Wash of Edmonton so gay.

And there he threw the Wash about on both sides of the way,
Just like unto a trundling mop, or a wild goose at play.
At Edmondton his loving wife, from the balcony espied
Her tender husband, wondering much to see how he did ride.

"Stop, stop, John Gilpin! here's the house!" they all aloud did cry;
"The dinner waits, and we are tired!" Said Gilpin, "So am I!"
But yet his horse was not a whit inclned to tarry there;
For why? his owner had a house full ten miles off, at Ware.

So like an arrow swift he flew, shot by an archer
strong,
So did he fly, — which brings me to the middle of my
song.
Away went Gilpin, out of breath, and sore against his
will,
Till at his friend the calender's his horse at last stood
still.

The calender, amazed to see his friend in such a trim,
Laid down his pipe, flew to the gate, and thus accosted
him:
" What news? What news? Your tidings tell! Tell me
you must and shall!
Say why bare-headed you are come, — or why you
come at all."

Now, Gilpin had a pleasant wit, and loved a timely
joke,
And thus unto the calender in merry guise he spoke:
" I came because your horse would come; and, if I well
forebode,
My hat and wig will soon be here; they are upon the
road!"

The calender, right glad to find his friend in merry pin,
Returned him not a single word, but to the house went
in,
Whence straight he came with hat and wig, — a wig
that flowed behind,
A hat not much the worse for wear, — each comely in
its kind.

He held them up, and in his turn thus showed his ready
  wit:
"My head is twice as big as yours: they therefore
  needs must fit.
But let me scrape the dust away that hangs upon your
  face;
And stop and eat, for well you may be in a hungry
  case."

Said John, "It is my wedding-day, and all the world
  would stare
If wife should dine at Edmonton and I should dine at
  Ware."
So, turning to his horse, he said, "I am in haste to dine;
'Twas for your pleasure you came here, you shall go
  back for mine."

Ah, luckless speech and bootless boast! for which he
  paid full dear;
For, while he spake a braying ass did sing out loud and
  clear,
Whereat his horse did snort as he had heard a lion roar,
And galloped off with all his might, as he had done before.

Away went Gilpin, and away went Gilpin's hat and
  wig;
He lost them sooner than at first; for why? — they
  were too big.
Now, Mrs. Gilpin, when she saw her husband posting
  down
Into the country far away, she pulled out half a crown.

And thus unto the youth she said that drove them to
   the Bell,
This shall be yours when you bring back my husband
   safe and well."
The youth did ride, and soon did meet John coming
   back amain,
Whom in a trice he tried to stop, by catching at his
   rein;

But, not performing what he meant, and gladly would
   have done,
The frighted steed he frighted more, and made him
   faster run.
Away went Gilpin, and away went post-boy at his
   heels,
The post-boy's horse right glad to miss the lumbering
   of the wheels.

Six gentlemen upon the road, thus seeing Gilpin fly,
With post-boy scampering in the rear, they raised the
   hue and cry,
"Stop thief! Stop thief!— a highwayman!"— not
   one of them was mute,
And all and each that passed that way did join in the
   pursuit.

And now the turnpike gates again flew open in short
   space,
The toll-man thinking, as before, that Gilpin rode a race.
And so he did, and won it too, for he got first to town,
Nor stopped till where he had got up he did again get
   down.

Now let us sing " long live the king," and Gilpin, long
    live he,
And when he next doth ride abroad may I be there to
    see!

THE PETERKINS CELEBRATE THE FOURTH OF JULY

(FROM THE PETERKIN PAPERS.)

By LUCRETIA P. HALE.

THE day began early.

A compact had been made with the little boys the evening before.

They were to be allowed to usher in the glorious day by the blowing of horns exactly at sunrise. But they were to blow them for precisely five minutes only, and no sound of the horns should be heard afterwards till the family were downstairs.

It was thought that a peace might thus be bought by a short, though crowded, period of noise.

The morning came. Even before the morning, at half-past three o'clock, a terrible blast of the horns aroused the whole family.

Mrs. Peterkin clasped her hands to her head and exclaimed: "I am thankful the lady from Philadelphia is not here!" For she had been invited to stay a week, but had declined to come before the Fourth of July, as she was not well, and her doctor had prescribed quiet.

And the number of the horns was most remarkable! It was as though every cow in the place had arisen and was blowing through both her own horns!

"How many little boys are there? How many have we?" exclaimed Mr. Peterkin, going over their names one by one mechanically, thinking he would do it, as he might count imaginary sheep jumping over a fence, to put himself to sleep. Alas! the counting could not put him to sleep now, in such a din.

And how unexpectedly long the five minutes seemed! Elizabeth Eliza was to take out her watch and give the signal for the end of the five minutes, and the ceasing of the horns. Why did not the signal come? Why did not Elizabeth Eliza stop them?

And certainly it was long before sunrise; there was no dawn to be seen!

"We will not try this plan again," said Mrs. Peterkin.

"If we live to another Fourth," added Mr. Peterkin, hastening to the door to inquire into the state of affairs.

Alas! Amanda, by mistake, had waked up the little boys an hour too early. And by another mistake the little boys had invited three or four of their friends to spend the night with them. Mrs. Peterkin had given them permission to have the boys for the whole day, and they understood the day as beginning when they went to bed the night before. This accounted for the number of horns.

It would have been impossible to hear any explanation; but the five minutes were over, and the horns had ceased, and there remained only the noise of a singular leaping of feet, explained perhaps by a possible pillow-fight, that kept the family below partially awake until the bells and cannon made known the dawning of the glorious day, — the sunrise, or the "rising of the sons," as Mr. Peterkin jocosely called it when they heard the little boys and their friends clattering down the stairs to begin the outside festivities.

They were bound first for the swamp, for Elizabeth Eliza, at the suggestion of the lady from Philadelphia, had advised them to hang some flags around the pillars of the piazza. Now the little boys knew of a place in the swamp where they had been in the habit of digging for "flag-root," and where they might find plenty of flag flowers. They did bring away all they could, but they were a little out of bloom. The boys were in the midst of nailing up all they had on the pillars of the piazza, when the procession of the Antiques and Horribles passed along. As the procession saw the festive arrangements on the piazza, and the crowd of boys, who cheered them loudly, it stopped to salute the house with some especial strains of greeting.

Poor Mrs. Peterkin! They were directly under her window! In a few moments of quiet, during the boys' absence from the house on their visit to the swamp, she had been trying to find out whether she had a sick-headache, or whether it was all the noise, and she was just deciding it was the sick headache, but was falling into a light slumber, when the fresh noise outside began.

There were the imitations of the crowing of cocks, and braying of donkeys, and the sound of horns, encored and increased by the cheers of the boys. Then began the torpedoes, and the Antiques and Horribles had Chinese crackers also.

And, in despair of sleep, the family came down to breakfast.

Mrs. Peterkin had always been much afraid of fire-works, and had never allowed the boys to bring gun-powder into the house. She was even afraid of torpe-does; they looked so much like sugar-plums she was sure some of the children would swallow them, and explode before anybody knew it.

She was very timid about other things. She was not sure even about peanuts. Everybody exclaimed over this: "Surely there was no danger in peanuts!" But Mrs. Peterkin declared she had been very much alarmed at the Centennial Exhibition, and in the crowded corners of the streets in Boston, at the peanut stands, where they had machines to roast the peanuts. She did not think it was safe. They might go off any time, in the midst of a crowd of people, too!

Mr. Peterkin thought there actually was no danger, and he should be sorry to give up the peanut. He thought it an American institution, something really belonging to the Fourth of July. He even confessed to a quiet pleasure in crushing the empty shells with his feet on the sidewalks as he went along the streets.

Agamemnon thought it a simple joy.

In consideration, however, of the fact that they had had no real celebration of the Fourth the last year, Mrs. Peterkin had consented to give over the day, this year, to the amusement of the family as a Centennial celebration. She would prepare herself for a terrible noise, — only she did not want any gunpowder brought into the house.

The little boys had begun by firing some torpedoes a few days beforehand, that their mother might be used to the sound, and had selected their horns some weeks before.

Solomon John had been very busy in inventing some fireworks. As Mrs. Peterkin objected to the use of gunpowder, he found out from the dictionary what the different parts of gunpowder are, — saltpetre, charcoal, and sulphur. Charcoal, he discovered, they had in the wood-house ; saltpetre they would find in the cellar, in the beef barrel; and sulphur they could buy at the apothecary's. He explained to his mother that these materials had never yet exploded in the house, and she was quieted.

Agamemnon, meanwhile, remembered a recipe he had read somewhere for making a "fulminating paste" of iron-filings and powder of brimstone. He had written it down on a piece of paper in his pocket-book. But the iron filings must be finely powdered. This they began upon a day or two before, and the very afternoon before laid out some of the paste on the piazza.

Pin-wheels and rockets were contributed by Mr. Peterkin for the evening. According to a programme drawn up by Agamemnon and Solomon John, the reading of the Declaration of Independence was to take place in the morning, on the piazza, under the flags.

The Bromwicks brought over their flag to hang over the door.

"That is what the lady from Philadelphia meant," explained Elizabeth Eliza.

"She said the flags of our country," said the little boys. "We thought she meant 'in the country.'"

Quite a company assembled; but it seemed nobody had a copy of the Declaration of Independence.

Elizabeth Eliza said she could say one line, if they each could add as much. But it proved they all knew the same line that she did, as they began: —

"When, in course of — when, in the course of — when, in the course of human — when in the course of

human events — when, in the course of human events,
it becomes — when, in the course of human events, it
becomes necessary — when, in the course of human
events, it becomes necessary for one people" —

They could not get any farther. Some of the party
decided that "one people" was a good place to stop,
and the little boys sent off some fresh torpedoes in
honor of the people. But Mr. Peterkin was not satisfied. He invited the assembled party to stay until sunset, and meanwhile he would find a copy, and torpedoes
were to be saved to be fired off at the close of every
sentence.

And now the noon bells rang and the noon bells
ceased.

Mrs. Peterkin wanted to ask everybody to dinner.
She should have some cold beef. She had let Amanda
go, because it was the Fourth, and everybody ought to
be free that one day ; so she could not have much of a
dinner. But when she went to cut her beef she found
Solomon had taken it to soak, on account of the saltpetre, for the fireworks !

Well, they had a pig; so she took a ham, and the
boys had bought tamarinds and buns and a cocoanut.
So the company stayed on, and when the Antiques and
Horribles passed again they were treated to peanuts
and lemonade.

They sung patriotic songs, they told stories, they
fired torpedoes, they frightened the cats with them. It
was a warm afternoon; the red poppies were out wide,
and the hot sun poured down on the alleyways in the
garden. There was a seething sound of a hot day in
the buzzing of insects, in the steaming heat that came

up from the ground.   Some neighboring boys were firing a toy cannon.   Every time it went off Mrs. Peterkin started, and looked to see if one of the little boys was gone.   Mr. Peterkin had set out to find a copy of the "Declaration."   Agamemnon had disappeared.   She had not a moment to decide about her headache.   She asked Ann Maria if she were not anxious about the fireworks, and if rockets were not dangerous.   They went up, but you were never sure where they came down.

And then came a fresh tumult! All the fire-engines in town rushed toward them, clanging with bells, men and boys yelling!   They were out for a practice, and for a Fourth-of-July show.

Mrs. Peterkin thought the house was on fire, and so did some of the guests.   There was great rushing hither and thither.   Some thought they would better go home; some thought they would better stay.   Mrs. Peterkin hastened into the house to save herself, or see what she could save.   Elizabeth Eliza followed her, first proceeding to collect all the pokers and tongs she could find, because they could be thrown out of the window without breaking.   She had read of people who had flung looking-glasses out of the window by mistake, in the excitement of the house being on fire, and had carried the pokers and tongs carefully into the garden.   There was nothing like being prepared.   She had always determined to do the reverse.   So with calmness she told Solomon John to take down the looking-glasses. But she met with a difficulty, — there were no pokers and tongs, as they did not use them.   They had no open fires; Mrs. Peterkin had been afraid of them.   So

Elizabeth Eliza took all the pots and kettles up to the upper windows, ready to be thrown out.

But where was Mrs. Peterkin? Solomon John found she had fled to the attic in terror. He persuaded her to come down, assuring her it was the most unsafe place; but she insisted upon stopping to collect some bags of old pieces, that nobody would think of saving from the general wreck, she said, unless she did. Alas! this was the result of fireworks on Fourth of July! As they came downstairs they heard the voices of all the company declaring there was no fire; the danger was past. It was long before Mrs. Peterkin could believe it. They told her the fire company was only out for show, and to celebrate the Fourth of July. She thought it already too much celebrated.

Elizabeth Eliza's kettles and pans had come down through the windows with a crash, that had only added to the festivities, the little boys thought.

Mr. Peterkin had been roaming about all this time in search of a copy of the Declaration of Independence. The public library was shut, and he had to go from house to house; but now, as the sunset bells and cannon began, he returned with a copy, and read it, to the pealing of the bells and sounding of the cannon. Torpedoes and crackers were fired at every pause. Some sweet-marjoram pots, tin cans filled with crackers which were lighted, went off with great explosions.

At the most exciting moment, near the close of the reading, Agamemnon, with an expression of terror, pulled Solomon John aside.

"I have suddenly remembered where I read about the 'fulminating paste' we made. It was in the preface to

' Woodstock,' and I have been round to borrow the book, to read the directions over again, because I was afraid about the ' paste ' going off. READ THIS QUICKLY ! and tell me, *Where is the fulminating paste ?* "

Solomon John was busy winding some covers of paper over a little parcel. It contained chlorate of potash and sulphur mixed. A friend had told him of the composition. The more thicknesses of paper you put round it the louder it would go off. You must pound it with a hammer. Solomon John felt it must be perfectly safe, as his mother had taken potash for a medicine.

He still held the parcel as he read from Agamemnon's book : " This paste, when it has lain together about twenty-six hours, will *of itself* take fire, and burn all the sulphur away with a blue flame and a bad smell.

" Where is the paste ? " repeated Solomon John, in terror.

" We made it just twenty-six hours ago," said Agamemnon.

" We put it on the piazza," exclaimed Solomon John, rapidly recalling the facts, " and it is in front of our mother's feet."

He hastened to snatch the paste away before it should take fire, flinging aside the packet in his hurry. Agamemnon, jumping upon the piazza at the same moment, trod upon the paper parcel, which exploded at once with the shock, and he fell to the ground, while at the same moment the paste " fulminated " into a blue flame directly in front of Mrs. Peterkin !

It was a moment of great confusion. There were cries and screams. The bells were still ringing, the cannon firing, and Mr. Peterkin had just reached the closing words: "Our lives, our fortunes, and our sacred honor."

"We are all blown up, as I feared we should be," Mrs. Peterkin at length ventured to say, finding herself in a lilac-bush by the side of the piazza. She scarcely dared to open her eyes to see the scattered limbs about her.

It was so with all. Even Ann Maria Bromwick clutched a pillar of the piazza, with closed eyes.

At length Mr. Peterkin said, calmly, "Is anybody killed?"

There was no reply. Nobody could tell whether it was because everybody was killed, or because they were too wounded to answer. It was a great while before Mrs. Peterkin ventured to move.

But the little boys soon shouted with joy, and cheered the success of Solomon John's fireworks, and hoped he had some more. One of them had his face blackened by an unexpected cracker, and Elizabeth Eliza's muslin dress was burned here and there. But no one was hurt; no one had lost any limbs, though Mrs. Peterkin was sure she had seen some flying in the air. Nobody could understand how, as she had kept her eyes firmly shut.

No greater accident had occurred than the singeing of the tip of Solomon John's nose. But there was an unpleasant and terrible odor from the "fulminating paste."

Mrs. Peterkin was extricated from the lilac-bush. No one knew how she got there. Indeed, the thundering noise had stunned everybody. It had roused the neighborhood even more than before. Answering explosions came on every side, and, though the sunset light had not faded away, the little boys hastened to send off rockets under cover of the confusion. Solomon John's other fireworks would not go. But all felt he had done enough.

Mrs. Peterkin retreated into the parlor, deciding she really did have a headache. At times she had to come out when a rocket went off, to see if it was one of the little boys. She was exhausted by the adventures of the day, and almost thought it could not have been worse if the boys had been allowed gunpowder. The distracted lady was thankful there was likely to be but one Centennial Fourth in her lifetime, and declared she should never more keep anything in the house as dangerous as saltpetred beef, and she should never venture to take another spoonful of potash.

THE REVEREND MR. TROTTY

(FROM THE TROTTY BOOK.)

BY ELIZABETH STUART PHELPS.

ONE Sunday it rained. Not that it never rained
on any other of Trotty's Sundays, but that it
did rain that especial Sunday.

Trotty sat on the window-sill, — it was a narrow
window-sill, and he kept slipping off with a little jerk,
and climbing up and slipping off, — feeling of the sash
with his eyelashes, and flattening his nose on the glass.
Great drops splashed and splattered down the panes;
little puddles stood on the sill; the trees blew about;
the road was wet, and the mud was deep.

"Come, Trotty," said Lill.

"Yes," said Trotty.

"Come, Trotty," said his mother, five minutes later.

"Yes'um," said Trotty; but he did not move.

"He's watching for Mr. Hymnal," exclaimed Lil;
"it is late for him; I wonder where he is."

Mr. Hymnal was going to preach that day; he drove
over from East Bampton on an exchange: he was to
dine with Trotty's mother, and Trotty felt burdened
with the entire responsibility of him.

.   .   .   .

Trotty was brushed and washed and dusted and tied
and buttoned and pinned at last; mamma was ready,

94

and Lill, and Max; the bell rang and the bell tolled, but Mr. Hymnal did not come.

"It must be the mud and hard driving that have delayed him," said mamma. "Very likely he will stop at the church without coming to the house; we won't wait any longer, I think."

Trotty began to look sober. When they came in sight of the church, he bobbed out from under Lill's umbrella and ran through the rain to his mother.

"Mamma, if the minister doesn't come, may I preach?"

"O yes," said Mrs. Tyrol, laughing at what she thought was some of "Trotty's fun." "You may preach," — and thought no more of what she said.

Mr. Hymnal's horse was not in the sheds; Mr. Hymnal was not in the pulpit. Trotty sat down in the tall box-pew and thought about it.

"I want the corner," said he to Max mysteriously, and Max, to please him, lifted him into the corner. The church was nearly full; the people began to grow still; the pulpit was yet empty. A door opened somewhere; Trotty kneeled on top of some hymn-books, and, turning around, looked attentively over the house. The blind organist had just come into the gallery, and was groping his way along with his cane, which made little taps on the floor. Trotty sat down again. In a minute another door opened, and a pew door flapped. Up went Trotty's curls and eyes again, where all the audience could see. It was old Mrs. Holt that time, — Mrs. Holt who was always late, and who wore the three-cornered green glasses, and walked like a horse going up hill. She tripped over a cricket as she went

into her pew, and Trotty's curls and eyes laughed out;
he never *could* help laughing at Mrs. Holt, — the people
saw him turn as pink as a rosebud, and disappear under
Max's arm. He felt so ashamed! Presently a door
opened again, and some very new boots creaked very
loudly up the whole length of the broad aisle. Up
jumped Trotty in a hurry now. Everybody thought
that they were the minister's boots, and so did he.
But it was only an old deacon in a black satin stock;
he sat down slowly, slowly buttoned his pew door,
slowly sunk his chin into his stock, and slowly and
severely coughed; a sort of slow astonishment that
everybody should be looking at him crept into his
wrinkles and his eyebrows. He concluded that he
must have put his wig on crookedly, and in feeling
around to find out he pulled it off.

But nobody else came in after that; the empty pulpit
stared down at the people; the people stared up at the
empty pulpit. Silence fell, deepened, grew painful,
grew awful, grew funny. Two small boys in the gallery smiled audibly. The old ladies put their hand-
kerchiefs to their mouths. The Deacon in the wig
looked at another Deacon; another Deacon looked at
them both; a fourth Deacon beckoned to the third
Deacon; then all the deacons whispered solemnly.

What was going to happen next?

Trotty had been sitting very still.

His mother, as it chanced, had her hand over her
eyes just then. Max was — well, to tell the truth, Max
was too busy in wishing that the veil on Nat's pretty
sister's pretty hat did not fall so far over her face to
notice much of anything else.

Suddenly they heard a stir. A choked laugh ran from slip to slip. Everybody was looking into the broad aisle and — Dear me! where was Trotty?

Out in the middle of the great empty aisle, with one hand stuck jauntily in the pocket of his little Zouave trousers, and a huge hymn-book in the other, with his cap on back side in front, ribbons and curls tossed into his eyes, dimple smoothed severely away, and a ministerial gravity on his pink chin, stood Trotty.

Before they knew what he was about, he was on the platform. Before they could reach him, he had begun to climb the pulpit stairs.

Just at that point he felt Max's hand upon his collar, and the next he knew he was securely buttoned into the pew again, at a safe distance from the door.

Could a young minister, on the occasion of preaching his first sermon, bear such a surprising turn of affairs with calmness? Was it not enough to quench the ambition of a lifetime, and ruffle the patience of the saints? Any clerical opinion on this point, if forwarded to the address of the Reverend Mr. Trotty, in my care, — or to me, in his care, — will be thankfully received, and duly appreciated.

"I was a goin' to preach," said Trotty, quite aloud, standing up in the pew, and squaring at Max with both fists. "You never pulled Mr. Hymnal round that way, you know you didn't! Now, I should like to know why you — "

"O hush, Trotty! hush!" His mother drew him down out of people's sight, but he turned on her with the quiet assurance of victory: —

"You said I might preach! You *said* I might, on ve

way over! Now we haven't got any minister, and it's just all your fault!"

Just then there was a noise at the green, muffled doors, and Mr. Hymnal came walking very fast up the aisle.

He could not imagine what all the people were laughing at.

He wondered so much, that he read the Missionary Hymn in this way, —

> "From Greenland's icy mountains,
> From India's coral strand,
> Where Afric's *soda fountains*
> Roll down their golden sand."

But somebody says I should not tell you how he read it, for fear that you may laugh the next time you hear it in church.

Under the circumstances, Mrs. Tyrol thought that Trotty had better stay at home that afternoon.

Feeling quite insulted, but a little too proud to say so, Trotty watched the rest walking off to the music of the ringing bells, and then sat down with Jerusalem to watch the rain. He amused himself for a while by counting the little dreary drops that rolled down the glass and melted away into the wet sill, but by and by that began to be dull work, and he told Jerusalem that he thought they had better go to church; he had a very good sermon, which he should have preached this morning if it hadn't been for that old Max; if Jerusalem would be a good boy and not knock the hymnbooks down, nor cry for candy, he might hear it now. Jerusalem bowed his empty head, — nothing came more

naturally to Jerusalem than making bows, — so Trotty
tied him into the high-chair, and himself mounted the
dining-room table, with a sofa-cushion, a Bible, and
Mother Goose, to preach.

That table made an excellent pulpit, — when Mamma
wasn't there to take it down! — and Jerusalem was as
quiet and attentive an audience as a clergyman could
ask for. Biddy was in the kitchen, and would have
been glad of an invitation, but Biddy had a way of
laughing in church which was very disagreeable. Trotty
thought that she could not have been taught, when she
was a little girl, to pay good attention to the sermon.

So Trotty preached to Jerusalem, and Jerusalem
listened to Trotty, half through the dark, wet, windy
afternoon. I am sorry not to have a phonographic report of that sermon, but Jerusalem, who gave me the
account of it, gave it from memory only, so that I fear
a large part of the minister's valuable thoughts are lost.
A few have been preserved in fragments, as follows: —

"My text will be found in the first chapter of Me-
thuselah: 'I love vem vat love me, and vose vat seek
me early sha'n't find me,' — sit still, Jerusalem! —
Moses was a very good man. 'Lijah went up in a
shariot of fire. I b'lieve I saw him one time last summer when there was a thunder-storm. — Jerusalem!
don't drum on 'e hymn-books in meeting time. Once
when I had a white kitty she died and went to heaven.
I know 'most she went to heaven, 'cause she was so
white, and she never scratched me but once. I don't
like dogs, not big black ones. They bark. I don't like
the dark either. Samuel was afraid of the dark. So'm
I. Now I lay me — *you* can't say, Now I lay me, Jeru-

salem! — Schildren, obey your parents, and unite in singing the 'leventh psalm: John Brown's Body, old metre: Amen."

Before the singing was over, the little minister espied a saucer of parched corn on the sideboard, and the idea struck him, what a nice stuffing it would make for Jerusalem's head. So, after telling the choir to keep right on, he climbed down from the pulpit, and began to drop the corns, one by one, into the doll's silk skull. This was great fun. When it was filled to the top, Jerusalem found that he could hold his head up as straight and stiff as other people. In fact, he might to this day have been able to look the world in the eye, if it had not been for the little circumstance, that, one by one, those corns mysteriously disappeared. Where they went to Jerusalem has never revealed; but the truth remains unquestioned, that before Mr. Trotty's sermon was over, that poor head hung despondent and empty. As for the saucer on the sideboard that was empty too.

When the real people came home from the real church, they found the Reverend Mr. Trotty drawing his audience noisily all over the house in a tip-cart.

"O, I'm sorry," said mamma, laying her gentle hand on his shoulder. "We don't play with tip-carts on God's Sunday."

"Well," said Trotty, after some thought, "you see I'm a little boy, and don't know any better!"

UP THE RIVER

(From Three Men in a Boat to Say Nothing of the Dog.)

By JEROME K. JEROME.

THERE were four of us — George, and William Samuel Harris, and myself, and Montmorency.

We were sitting in my room, smoking and talking about how bad we were — bad from a medical point of view I mean, of course. . . .

George said : —

" Let's go up the river."

He said we should have fresh air, exercise, and quiet ; the constant change of scene would occupy our minds (including what there was of Harris's), and the hard work would give us a good appetite and make us sleep well. . . .

Harris and I both said it was a good idea of George's ; and we said it in a tone that seemed to somehow imply that we were surprised that George should have come out so sensible.

The only one who was not struck with the suggestion

was Montmorency. He never did care for the river, did Montmorency.

"It's all very well for you fellows," he said; "you like it, but I don't. There's nothing for me to do. Scenery is not in my line, and I don't smoke. If I see a rat you won't stop, and if I get to sleep you get fooling about with the boat and slop me overboard. If you ask me I call the whole thing bally foolishness."

We were three to one, however, and the motion was carried. . . .

So, on the following evening, we again assembled to discuss and arrange our plans. Harris said : —

"Now, the first thing to settle is what to take with us. Now, you get a bit of paper and write down, J., and you get the grocery catalogue, George, and somebody give me a bit of pencil, and then I'll make out a list."

That's Harris all over — so ready to take the burden of everything himself and put it on the backs of other people.

He always reminds me of my poor uncle Podger. You never saw such a commotion up and down a house in all your life as when my Uncle Podger undertook to do the job. A picture would have come home from the frame-maker's and be standing in the dining-room, waiting to be put up, and Aunt Podger would ask what was to be done with it, and Uncle Podger would say : —

"Oh, you leave that to me. Don't you, any of you, worry yourselves about that. I'll do all that."

And then he would take off his coat and begin. He would send the girl out for sixpen'orth of nails, and then one of the boys after her to tell her what size to get, and from that he would gradually work down and start the whole house.

" Now, you go and get me a hammer, Will," he would shout; " and you bring me the rule, Tom ; and I shall want the step-ladder, and I had better have a kitchen chair, too ; and Jim ! you run round to Mr. Goggles and tell him, ' Pa's kind regards and hopes his leg's better, and will he lend him his spirit level ? ' And don't you go, Maria, because I shall want somebody to hold me the light ; and when the girl comes back she must go out again for a bit of picture-cord : and Tom — where's Tom ? — Tom, you come here ; I shall want you to hand me up the picture."

And then he would lift up the picture, and drop it, and it would come out of the frame, and he would try to save the glass and cut himself ; and then he would spring round the room, looking for his handkerchief. He could not find his handkerchief because it was in the pocket of the coat he had taken off, and he didn't know where he had put the coat, and all the house had to leave off looking for his tools and start looking for his coat, while he would dance round and hinder them.

" Doesn't anybody in the whole house know where my coat is ? I never came across such a set in all my life — upon my word I didn't. Six of you ! — and you can't find a coat that I put down not five minutes ago ! Well, of all the — "

Then he'd get up and find he had been sitting on it, and would call out : —

" Oh, you can give it up ! I've found it myself now.

Might just as well ask the cat to find anything as expect you people to find it."

And, when a half an hour had been spent in tying up his finger and a new glass had been got, and the tools, and the ladder, and the chair, and the candle had been brought, he would have another go, the whole family, including the girl and the charwoman, standing round in a semicircle, ready to help. Two people would have to hold the chair, and a third would help him up on it and hold him there, and the fourth would hand him a nail, and a fifth would pass him up the hammer, and he would take hold of the nail and drop it.

"There!" he would say, in an injured tone, "now the nail's gone."

And we would all have to go down on our knees and grovel for it while he would stand on a chair and grunt and want to know if he was to be kept there all the evening.

The nail would be found at last, and by that time he would have lost the hammer.

"Where's the hammer? What did I do with the hammer? Great heavens! Seven of you, gaping round there, and you don't know what I did with the hammer!"

We would find the hammer for him, and then he would have lost sight of the mark he had made on the wall, where the nail was to go in, and each of us had to get up on a chair beside him and see if we could find it, and we would each discover it in a different place, and he would call us all fools, one after another, and tell us to get down. And he would take the rule and re-measure and find that he wanted half thirty-one and three-eighths inches from the corner and would try to do it in his head and go mad.

And we would all try to do it in our heads and all arrive at different results and sneer at one another. And in the general row the original number would be forgotten, and Uncle Podger would have to measure it again.

He would use a bit of string this time, and at the critical moment, when the old fool was leaning over the chair at an angle of forty-five degrees and was trying to reach a point three inches beyond what was possible for him to reach, the string would slip, and down he would slide on to the piano, a really fine musical effect being produced by the suddenness with which his head and body struck all the notes at the same time.

And Aunt Maria would say that she would not allow the children to stand round and hear such language.

At last Uncle Podger would get the spot fixed again, and put the point of the nail on it with his left hand and take the hammer in his right hand. And with the first blow he would smash his thumb and drop the hammer, with a yell, on somebody's toes.

Aunt Maria would mildly observe that next time Uncle Podger was going to hammer a nail into the wall she hoped he'd let her know in time, so that she could make arrangements to go and spend a week with her mother while it was being done.

" Oh ! you women, you make such a fuss over everything," Uncle Podger would reply, picking himself up. " Why, I like doing a little job of this sort."

And then he would have another try, and, at the

second blow, the nail would go clean through the plaster and half the hammer after it, and Uncle Podger be precipitated against the wall with force nearly sufficient to flatten his nose.

Then we would have to find the rule and the string again, and a new hole would be made; and about midnight the picture would be up — very crooked and insecure, the wall for yards around looking as if it had been smoothed down with a rake, and everybody dead beat and wretched — except Uncle Podger.

"There you are," he would say, stepping heavily off the chair onto the charwoman's corns and surveying the mess he had made with evident pride. "Why, some people would have a man in to do a little thing like that!" . . .

"WE MADE A LIST OF THE THINGS TO BE TAKEN."

We made a list of the things to be taken, and a pretty lengthy one it was, before we parted that evening. The next day, which was Friday, we got them all together, and met in the evening to pack. We got a big Gladstone for the clothes, and a couple of hampers for the victuals and the cooking utensils. We moved the table up against the window, piled everything in a heap in the middle of the floor, and sat round and looked at it. I said I'd pack.

I rather pride myself on my packing. Packing is one of those many things that I feel I know more about than any other person living. (It surprises me myself, sometimes, how many of these subjects there are.) I impressed the fact upon George and Harris, and told them they had better leave the whole matter entirely to me. They fell into the suggestion with a readiness that had something uncanny about it. George put on a pipe and spread himself over the easy-chair, and Harris cocked his legs on the table and lit a cigar.

This was hardly what I intended. What I had meant, of course, was, that I should boss the job, and that Harris and George should potter about under my directions, I pushing them aside every now and then with, " Oh, you ! " — " Here, let me do it." " There you are, simple enough ! " really teaching them, as you might say. Their taking it in the way they did irritated me. There is nothing does irritate me more than seeing other people sitting about doing nothing when I'm working.

I lived with a man once who used to make me mad that way. He would loll on the sofa and watch me doing things by the hour together, following me round the room with his eyes, wherever I went. He said it did him real good to look on at me, messing about. He said it made him feel that life was not an idle dream to be gaped and yawned through, but a noble task, full of duty and stern work. He said he often wondered now how he could have gone on before he met me, never having anybody to look at while they worked.

Now, I'm not like that. I can't sit still and see another man slaving and working. I want to get up and superintend, and walk round with my hands in my pockets, and tell what to do. It is my energetic nature. I can't help it.

II-5

However, I did not say anything, but started the packing. It seemed a longer job than I had thought it was going to be, but I got the bag finished at last, and I sat on it and strapped it.

"Ain't you going to put the boots in?" said Harris.

And I looked round and found I had forgotten them. That's just like Harris. He couldn't have said a word until I'd got the bag shut and strapped, of course. And George laughed — one of those irritating, senseless, chuckle-headed, crack-jawed laughs of his. They do make me so wild.

I opened the bag and packed the boots in; and then, just as I was going to close it, a horrible idea occurred to me. Had I packed my tooth-brush? I don't know how it is, but I never do know whether I've packed my tooth-brush.

My tooth-brush is a thing that haunts me when I'm travelling, and makes my life a misery. I dream that I haven't packed it, and wake up in a cold perspiration, and get out of bed and hunt for it. And, in the morning, I pack it before I have used it, and have to unpack again to get it, and it is always the last thing I turn out of the bag; and then I repack and forget it, and have to rush upstairs for it at the last moment and carry it to the railway station, wrapped up in my pocket-handkerchief.

Of course I had to turn every mortal thing out now, and, of course, I could not find it. I rummaged the things up into much the same state that they must have been in before the world was created, and when chaos reigned. Of course, I found George's and Harris's eighteen times over, but I couldn't find my

own. I put the things back one by one, and held
everything up and shook it. Then I found it inside a
boot. I repacked once more.

When I had finished, George asked me if the soap was
in. I said I didn't care a hang whether the soap was
in or whether it wasn't; and I slammed the bag to and
strapped it, and found that I had
packed my tobacco pouch in it
and had to reopen it. It got shut
up finally at 10.05 P.M., and then
there remained the hampers to
do. Harris said that we should
be wanting to start in less than
twelve hours' time, and thought
that he and
George had bet-
ter do the rest;
and I agreed and
sat down, and
they had a go.

They began in
a light-hearted
spirit, evidently
intending to
show me how to

I HAD TO TURN EVERY MORTAL THING OUT.

do it. I made no comment. I only waited. When
George is hanged, Harris will be the worst packer in
this world; and I looked at the piles of plates and
cups, and kettles, and bottles and jars, and pies, and
stoves, and cakes, and tomatoes, etc., and felt that the
thing would soon become exciting.

It did. They started with breaking a cup. That

was the first thing they did. They did that just to show you what they could do, and to get you interested.

Then Harris packed the strawberry jam on top of a tomato and squashed it, and they had to pick out the tomato with a teaspoon.

And then it was George's turn, and he trod on the butter. I didn't say anything, but I came over and sat on the edge of the table and watched them. It irritated them more than anything I could have said. I felt that. It made them nervous and excited, and they stepped on things, and put things behind them, and then couldn't find them when they wanted them; and they packed the pies at the bottom, and put heavy things on top, and smashed the pies in.

· They upset salt over everything, and as for the butter! I never saw two men do more with one-and-two-pence worth of butter in my whole life than they did. After George had got it off his slipper, they tried to put it in the kettle. It wouldn't go in, and what was in wouldn't come out. They did scrape it out at last, and put it down on a chair, and Harris sat on it, and it stuck to him, and they went looking for it all over the room.

"I'll take my oath I put it down on that chair," said George, staring at the empty seat.

"I saw you do it myself, not a minute go," said Harris.

Then they started round the room again looking for it; and then they met again in the centre, and stared at one another.

"Most extraordinary thing I ever heard of," said George.

" So mysterious ! " said Harris.

Then George got around at the back of Harris and saw it.

" Why, here it is all the time," he exclaimed indignantly.

" Where? " cried Harris, spinning round.

" Stand still, can't you ! " roared George, flying after him.

And they got it off, and packed it in the teapot.

Montmorency was in it all, of course. Montmorency's ambition in life is to get in the way and be sworn at. If he can squirm in anywhere where he particularly is not wanted, and be a perfect nuisance, and make people mad, and have things thrown at his head, then he feels his day has not been wasted.

To get somebody to stumble over him, and curse him steadily for an hour, is his highest aim and object ; and, when he has succeeded in accomplishing this, his conceit becomes quite unbearable.

He came and sat down on things, just when they were wanted to be packed; and he labored under the fixed belief that, whenever Harris or George reached out their hand for anything, it was his cold, damp nose that they wanted. He put his leg into the jam, and he worried the teaspoons, and he pretended that the lemons were rats, and got into the hamper and killed three of them before Harris could land him with the frying-pan.

Harris said I encouraged him. I didn't encourage him. A dog like that doesn't want any encouragement. It's the natural, original sin that is born in him that makes him do things like that.

The packing was done at 12.50 ; and Harris sat on the big hamper, and said he hoped nothing would be found broken. George said that if anything was broken, it was broken, which reflection seemed to comfort him. He also said he was ready for bed. We were all ready for bed.

.   .   .   .

I awoke at six the next morning, and found George awake, too. We both turned round, and tried to go to sleep again, but we could not. Had there been any particular reason why we should not have gone to sleep again, but have got up and dressed then and there, we should have dropped off while we were looking at our watches, and have slept till ten. As there was no earthly necessity for our getting up under another two hours at the very least, and our getting up at that time was an utter absurdity, it was only in keeping with the natural wickedness of things in general that we should both feel that lying down for five minutes more would be death to us.

George said that the same kind of thing, only worse, had happened to him some eighteen months ago, when he was lodging by himself in the house of a certain Mrs. Gippings. He said his watch went wrong one evening, and stopped at a quarter-past eight. He did not know this at the time because, for some reason or other, he forgot to wind it up when he went to bed (an unusual occurrence with him) and hung it up over his pillow without ever looking at the thing.

It was in the winter when this happened, very near the shortest day, and a week after into the bargain, so the fact that it was still very dark when George woke in the morning was no guide to him as to the time. He reached up, and hauled down his watch. It was a quarter-past eight.

"Angels and ministers of grace defend us!" exclaimed George, "and here I have got to be in the city by nine. Why didn't somebody call me? Oh, this is a shame!" And he flung the watch down, and sprang out of bed, and had a cold bath, and washed himself, and dressed himself, and shaved himself in cold water because there was not time to wait for the hot, and then rushed and had another look at the watch.

Whether the shaking it had received in being thrown on the bed had started it, or how it was, George could not say; but certain it was that from a quarter-past eight it had begun to go, and now pointed to twenty minutes to nine.

George snatched it up, and rushed down-stairs. In the sitting-room all was dark and silent: there was no fire, no breakfast. George said it was a wicked shame of Mrs. G., and he made up his mind to tell her what he thought of her when he came home in the evening. Then he dashed on his greatcoat and hat, and, seizing his umbrella, made for the front door. The door was not even unbolted.

George anathematized Mrs. G. for a lazy old woman, and thought it was very strange that people could not get up at a decent, respectable time, unlocked and unbolted the door, and ran out.

He ran hard for a quarter of a mile, and at the end of that distance it began to be borne in upon him as a strange and curious thing that there were so few people about, and that there were no shops open. It was certainly a very dark and foggy morning, but still it seemed an unusual course to stop all business on that account. He had to go to business: why should other people stop in bed merely because it was dark and foggy!

At length he reached Holborn. Not a shutter was down! not a bus was about! There were three men in sight, one of whom was a policeman; a market-cart full of cabbages and a dilapidated-looking cab. George pulled out his watch and looked at it: it was five minutes to nine!

He stood still and counted his pulse. He stooped down and felt his legs. Then, with his watch still in his hand, he went up to the policeman and asked him if he knew what the time was.

"What's the time?" said the man, eying George up and down with evident suspicion; "why, if you listen you will hear it strike."

George listened, and a neighboring clock immediately obliged.

IN THE EASY CHAIR.

"But it's only gone three!" said George in an injured tone, when it had finished.

"Well, and how many did you want it to go?" replied the constable.

"Why, nine," said George, showing his watch.

"Do you know where you live?" said the guardian of public order, severely.

George thought, and gave the address.

"Oh, that's where it is, is it?" replied the man; "well, you take my advice and go there quietly, and take that watch of yours with you ; and don't let's have any more of it."

And George went home again, musing as he walked along, and let himself in.

At first, when he got in, he determined to undress and go to bed again; but when he thought of re-dressing and re-washing, and the having of another bath, he determined he would not, but would sit up and go to sleep in the easy chair.

But he could not get to sleep: he never felt more wakeful in his life; so he lit the lamp and got out the chess-board, and played himself a game of chess. But even that did not enliven him : it seemed slow somehow; so he gave chess up and tried to read. He did not seem able to take any sort of interest in reading either, so he put on his coat again and went out for a walk.

It was horribly lonesome and dismal, and all the policemen he met regarded him with undisguised suspicion, and turned their lanterns on him and followed him about; and this had such an effect upon him at last, that he began to feel as if he really had done something, and he got to slinking down the by-streets and hiding in dark doorways when he heard the regulation flip-flop approaching.

Of course, this conduct made the force only more distrustful of him than ever, and they would come and rout him out and ask him what he was doing there; and when he answered, "Nothing," he had merely come out for a stroll (it was then four o'clock in the morning), they looked as though they did not believe him, and two plain-clothes constables came home with him to see if he really did live where he had said he did. They saw him go in with his key, and then they took up a position opposite and watched the house.

He thought he would light the fire when he got inside, and make himself some breakfast, just to pass away the time; but he did not seem able to handle anything from a scuttleful of coal to a teaspoon without dropping it or falling over it, and making such a noise that he was in mortal fear that it would wake Mrs. G. up, and that she would think it was burglars and open the window and call "Police!" and then these two detectives would rush in and handcuff him, and march him off to the police court.

He was in a morbidly nervous state by this time, and he pictured the trial, and his trying to explain the circumstances to the jury, and nobody believing him, and his being sentenced to twenty years' penal servitude, and his mother dying of a broken heart. So he gave up trying to get breakfast, and wrapped himself up in his overcoat and sat in the easy chair till Mrs. G. came down at half-past seven.

He said he had never got up too early since that morning: it had been such a warning to him.

It was a glorious day, and the lock was crowded; and, as is a common practice up the river, a speculative photographer was taking a picture of us all as we lay upon the rising waters.

I did not catch what was going on at first, and was, therefore, extremely surprised at noticing George hurriedly smooth out his trousers, ruffle up his hair, and stick his cap on in a rakish manner at the back of his head, and then, assuming an expression of mingled affability and sadness, sit down in a graceful attitude, and try to hide his feet.

My first idea was that he had suddenly caught sight of some girl he knew, and I looked about to see who it was. Everybody in the lock seemed to have been suddenly struck wooden. They were all standing or sitting about in the most quaint and curious attitudes I have ever seen off a Japanese fan. All the girls were smiling. Oh, they did look so sweet! And all the fellows were frowning, and looking stern and noble.

And then, at last, the truth flashed across me, and I wondered if I should be in time. Ours was the first boat, and it would be unkind of me to spoil the man's picture, I thought.

So I faced round quickly, and took up a position in the prow, where I leant with careless grace upon the hitcher, in an attitude suggestive of agility and strength. I arranged my hair with a curl over the forehead, and threw an air of tender wistfulness into my expression, mingled with a touch of cynicism, which I am told suits me.

As we stood waiting for the eventful moment, I heard some one behind call out:

"Hi! look at your nose."

I could not turn round to see what was the matter, and whose nose it was that was to be looked at. I stole a side glance at George's nose! It was all right — at all events there was nothing wrong with it that

could be altered. I squinted down at my own, and
that seemed all that could be expected also.

"Look at your nose, you stupid ass!" came the
same voice again, louder.

And then another voice cried:

"Push your nose out, can't you, you — you two with
the dog!"

Neither George nor I dared to turn round. The
man's hand was on the cap, and the picture might be
taken any moment. Was it us they were calling to?
What was the matter with our noses? Why were they
to be pushed out!

But now the whole lock started yelling, and a sten-
torian voice from the back shouted: —

"Look at your boat, sir; you in the red and black
caps. It's your two corpses that will get taken into
that photo, if you ain't quick."

We looked then, and saw that the nose of our boat
had got fixed under the woodwork of the lock while
the incoming water was rising all round it, and tilting
it up. In another moment we should be over. Quick
as thought, we each seized an oar, and a vigorous blow
against the side of the lock with the butt-ends released
the boat. and sent us sprawling on our backs.

We didn't come out well in that photograph, George
and I. Of course, as was to be expected, our luck or-
dained it that the man should set his wretched machine
in motion at the precise moment that we were both
lying on our backs with a wild expression of "Where
am I? and what is it?" on our faces, and our four
feet waving madly in the air.

Our feet were undoubtedly the leading articles in

that photograph. Indeed, very little else was to be seen. They filled up the foreground entirely. Behind them, you caught glimpes of the other boats, and bits of the surrounding scenery; but everything and everybody else in the lock looked so utterly insignificant and paltry compared with our feet, that all the other people felt quite ashamed of themselves, and refused to subscribe to the picture.

The owner of one steam launch, who had bespoke six copies, rescinded the order on seeing the negative. He said he would take them if anybody could show him his launch, but nobody could. It was somewhere behind George's right foot.

There was a good deal of unpleasantness over the business. The photographer thought that we ought to take a dozen copies each, seeing that the photo was about nine-tenths us, but we declined. We said we had no objection to being photo'd full length, but we preferred being taken the right way up.

QUEEN ALICE

(From Through the Looking-Glass.)

By LEWIS CARROLL.

ELL, this *is* grand!" said Alice. "I never expected I should be a Queen so soon — and I'll tell you what it is, your majesty," she went on in a severe tone (she was always rather fond of scolding herself), "it'll never do for you to be lolling about on the grass like that! Queens have to be dignified, you know!"

So she got up and walked about — rather stiffly just at first, as she was afraid that the crown might come off: but she comforted herself with the thought that there was nobody to see her, "and if I really am a Queen," she said, as she sat down again, "I shall be able to manage it quite well in time."

Everything was happening so oddly that she didn't feel a bit surprised at finding the Red Queen and the White Queen sitting close to her, one on each side: she would have liked very much to ask them how they came there, but she feared it would not be quite civil. However, there would be no harm, she thought, in asking if the game was over.

"Please, would you tell me —— " she began, looking timidly at the Red Queen.

"Speak when you're spoken to!" the Queen sharply interrupted her.

"But if everybody obeyed that rule," said Alice, who was always ready for a little argument, "and if you only spoke when you were spoken to, and the other person always waited for *you* to begin, you see nobody would ever say anything, so that——"

"Ridiculous!" cried the Queen. "Why, don't you see, child——" here she broke off with a frown, and, after thinking for a minute, suddenly changed the subject of the conversation. "What do you mean by 'If you really are a Queen'? What right have you to call yourself so? You can't be a Queen, you know, till you've passed the proper examination. And the sooner we begin it, the better."

"I only said 'if,'" poor Alice pleaded in a piteous tone.

The two Queens looked at each other, and the Red Queen remarked, with a little shudder, "She *says* she only said 'if'——"

"But she said a great deal more than that," the White Queen moaned, wringing her hands. "Oh, ever so much more than that."

"So you did, you know," the Red Queen said to Alice. "Always speak the truth—think before you speak—and write it down afterward."

"I'm sure I didn't mean——" Alice was beginning, but the Red Queen interrupted her impatiently.

"That's just what I complain of. You *should* have meant! What do you suppose is the use of a child without any meaning? Even a joke should have some meaning—and a child's more important than a joke, I hope. You couldn't deny that, even if you tried with both hands."

" I don't deny things with my *hands*," Alice objected.

" Nobody said you did," said the Red Queen. " I said you couldn't if you tried."

" She's in that state of mind," said the White Queen, " that she wants to deny *something* — only she doesn't know what to deny."

" A nasty, vicious temper," the Red Queen remarked; and then there was an uncomfortable silence for a minute or two.

The Red Queen broke the silence by saying to the White Queen, " I invite you to Alice's dinner-party this afternoon."

The White Queen smiled feebly, and said " And I invite *you*."

" I didn't know I was to have a party at all," said Alice; " but if there is to be one, I think *I* ought to invite the guests."

" We gave you the opportunity of doing it," the Red Queen remarked: " but I dare say you've not had many lessons in manners yet."

" Manners are not taught in lessons," said Alice. " Lessons teach you to do sums, and things of that sort."

"Can you do Addition?" the White Queen asked. " What's one and one and one and one and one and one and one and one and one and one ? "

" I don't know," said Alice. " I lost count."

"She can't do Addition," the Red Queen interrupted. "Can you do Subtraction? Take nine from eight."

" Nine from eight I can't, you know," Alice replied
very readily : " but —— "

" She can't do Subtraction," said the White Queen.
" Can you do Division ?   Divide a loaf by a knife —
what's the answer to that ? "

" I suppose —— " Alice was beginning, but the Red
Queen answered for her.   " Bread-and-butter, of course.
Try another Subtrac-
tion sum.   Take a
bone from a dog :
what remains ? "

Alice consid-
ered.   " The
bone wouldn't
remain, of
course, if I
took it — and
the dog wouldn't remain ; it would come to bite me —
and I'm sure *I* shouldn't remain ! "

" Then you think nothing would remain ? " said the
Red Queen.

" I think that's the answer."

" Wrong as usual," said the Red Queen.   " The dog's
temper would remain."

" But I don't see how —— "

" Why, look here ! " the Red Queen cried.   " The
dog would lose its temper, wouldn't it ? "

" Perhaps it would," Alice replied cautiously.

" Then if the dog went away, its temper would remain ! " the Queen exclaimed triumphantly.

Alice said, as gravely as she could, " They might
go different ways."   But she couldn't help thinking

to herself, "What dreadful nonsense we *are* talking!"

"She can't do sums a *bit!*" the Queens said together, with great emphasis.

"Can *you* do sums?" Alice said, turning suddenly on the White Queen, for she didn't like being found fault with so much.

The Queen gasped and shut her eyes. "I can do Addition," she said, "if you give me time — but I can't do Subtraction under *any* circumstances!"

"Of course you know your A B C?" said the Red Queen.

"To be sure I do," said Alice.

"So do I," the White Queen whispered: "we'll often say it over together, dear. And I'll tell you a secret — I can read words of one letter! Isn't *that* grand? However, don't be discouraged. You'll come to it in time."

Here the Red Queen began again. "Can you answer useful questions?" she said. "How is bread made?"

"I know *that!*" Alice cried eagerly. "You take some flour ——"

"Where do you pick the flower?" the White Queen asked. "In a garden, or in the hedges?"

"Well, it isn't *picked* at all," Alice explained: "it's *ground* ——"

"How many acres of ground?" said the White Queen. "You mustn't leave out so many things."

"Fan her head!" the Red Queen anxiously interrupted. "She'll be feverish after so much thinking." So they set to work and fanned her with bunches of

" 'What Is It Now?' the Frog Said in a Deep Hoarse Whisper."

leaves, till she had to beg them to leave off, it blew her hair about so.

" She's all right again now," said the Red Queen. " Do you know Languages? What's the French for fiddle-de-dee ? "

" Fiddle-de-dee's not English," Alice replied gravely.

" Who ever said it was ? " said the Red Queen.

Alice thought she saw a way out of the difficulty this time. " If you'll tell me what language ' fiddle-de-dee ' is, I'll tell you the French for it ! " she exclaimed triumphantly.

But the Red Queen drew herself up rather stiffly, and said, " Queens never make bargains."

" I wish Queens never asked questions," Alice thought to herself.

" Don't let us quarrel," the White Queen said, in an anxious tone. " What is the cause of lightning ? "

" The cause of lightning," Alice said, very decidedly, for she felt quite certain about this, " is the thunder — no, no ! " she hastily corrected herself. " I meant the other way."

" It's too late to correct it," said the Red Queen: " when you've once said a thing, that fixes it, and you must take the consequences."

" Which reminds me," the White Queen said, looking down and nervously clasping and unclasping her hands, " we had *such* a thunderstorm last Tuesday — I mean one of the last set of Tuesdays, you know."

Alice was puzzled. " In *our* country," she remarked, " there's only one day at a time."

The Red Queen said " That's a poor thin way of

doing things. Now *here,* we mostly have days and nights two or three at a time, and sometimes in the winter we take as many as five nights together — for warmth, you know."

" Are five nights warmer than one night, then?" Alice ventured to ask.

" Five times as warm, of course."

" But they should be five times as *cold,* by the same rule —— "

" Just so ! " cried the Red Queen. " Five times as warm, *and* five times as cold — just as I'm five times as rich as you are, *and* five times as clever ! "

Alice sighed and gave it up. " It's exactly like a riddle with no answer ! " she thought.

" Humpty Dumpty saw it too," the White Queen went on in a low voice, more as if she were talking to herself. " He came to the door with a corkscrew in his hand —— "

" What did he want? " said the Red Queen.

" He said he *would* come in," the White Queen went on, "because he was looking for a hippopotamus. Now, as it happened, there wasn't such a thing in the house that morning."

" Is there generally? " Alice asked in an astonished tone.

" Well, only on Thursdays," said the Queen.

" I know what he came for," said Alice : " he wanted to punish the fish, because —— "

Here the White Queen began again. " It was *such* a thunderstorm, you can't think ! " (" She *never* could, you know," said the Red Queen.) " And part of the roof came off, and ever so much thunder got in

— and it went rolling round the room in great lumps — and knocking over the tables and things — till I was so frightened, I couldn't remember my own name!"

Alice thought to herself, "I never should *try* to remember my name in the middle of an accident! Where would be the use of it?" but she did not say this aloud, for fear of hurting the poor Queen's feelings.

"Your Majesty must excuse her," the Red Queen said to Alice, taking one of the White Queen's hands in her own, and gently stroking it: "she means well, but she can't help saying foolish things, as a general rule."

The White Queen looked timidly at Alice, who felt she *ought* to say something kind, but really couldn't think of anything at the moment.

"She never was really well brought up," the Red Queen went on: "but it's amazing how good tempered she is! Pat her on the head, and see how pleased she'll be!" But this was more than Alice had courage to do.

"A little kindness — and putting her hair in papers — would do wonders with her——"

The White Queen gave a deep sigh, and laid her head on Alice's shoulder. "I *am* so sleepy!" she moaned.

"She's tired, poor thing!" said the Red Queen. "Smooth her hair — lend her your nightcap — and sing her a soothing lullaby."

"I haven't got a nightcap with me," said Alice, as she tried to obey the first direction: "and I don't know any soothing lullabies."

"I must do it myself, then," said the Red Queen, and she began:

> "Hush-a-by lady, in Alice's lap!
>   Till the feast's ready, we've time for a nap:
> When the feast's over, we'll go to the ball—
>   Red Queen, and White Queen, and Alice, and all!

"And now you know the words," she added, as she put her head down on Alice's other shoulder, "just sing it through to *me*, I'm getting sleepy, too." In another moment both Queens were fast asleep, and snoring loud.

"What *am* I to do?" exclaimed Alice, looking about in great perplexity, as first one round head, and then the other, rolled down from her shoulder, and lay like a heavy lump in her lap. "I don't think it *ever* happened before, that any one had to take care of two queens asleep at once! No, not in all the History of England — it couldn't, you know, because there never was more than one Queen at a time. Do wake up, you heavy things!" she went on in an impatient tone; but there was no answer but a gentle snoring.

The snoring got more distinct every minute, and sounded more like a tune: at last she could even make out words and she listened so eagerly that when the two great heads suddenly vanished from her lap, she hardly missed them.

She was standing before an arched doorway over which were the words QUEEN ALICE in large letters, and on each side of the arch there was a bell handle: one was marked " Visitor's Bell," and the other "Servant's Bell."

" I'll wait till the song's over," thought Alice, "and then I'll ring the — the — *which* bell must I ring?" she went on, very much puzzled by the names. "I'm not a visitor, and I'm not a servant. There *ought* to be one marked ' Queen,' you know —— "

Just then the door opened a little way, and a creature with a long beak put its head out for a moment and said "No admittance till the week after next!" and shut the door again with a bang.

Alice knocked and rang in vain for a long time, but at last a very old Frog, who was sitting under a tree, got up and hobbled slowly toward her : he was dressed in bright yellow, and had enormous boots on.

" What is it now?" the Frog said in a deep hoarse whisper.

Alice turned round, ready to find fault with anybody. "Where's the servant whose business it is to answer the door?" she began angrily.

" Which door?" said the Frog.

Alice almost stamped with irritation at the slow drawls in which he spoke. " *This* door, of course!"

The Frog looked at the door with his large dull eyes for a minute : then he went nearer and rubbed it with his thumb, as if he were trying whether the paint would come off, then he looked at Alice.

" To answer the door ? " he said. " What's it been asking of ? " He was so hoarse that Alice could scarcely hear him.

" I don't know what you mean," she said.

" I speaks English, doesn't I ? " the Frog went on. " Or are you deaf ? What did it ask you ? "

" Nothing ! " Alice said impatiently. " I've been knocking at it ! "

" Shouldn't do that — shouldn't do that," the Frog muttered. " Wexes it, you know." Then he went up and gave the door a kick with one of his great feet. " You let *it* alone," he panted out, as he hobbled back to his tree, " and it'll let *you* alone, you know."

At this moment the door was flung open, and a shrill voice was heard singing :

" To the Looking-Glass world it was Alice that said,
  ' I've a sceptre in hand, I've a crown on my head ;
Let the Looking-Glass creatures, whatever they be,
Come and dine with the Red Queen, the White Queen, and
  me ! ' "

And hundreds of voices joined in the chorus :

  " Then fill up the glasses as quick as you can,
    And sprinkle the table with buttons and bran ;
    Put cats in the coffee, and mice in the tea —
    And welcome Queen Alice with thirty-times-three ! "

Then followed a confused noise of cheering, and Alice thought to herself, " Thirty times three makes ninety. I wonder if any one's counting ? " In a minute there was silence again, and the same shrill voice sang another verse :

" ' O Looking-Glass creatures,' quoth Alice, ' draw near !
'Tis an honor to see me, a favor to hear ;
'Tis a privilege high to have dinner and tea
Along with the Red Queen, the White Queen and me ! ' "

Then came the chorus again :

" Then fill up the glasses with treacle and ink,
   Or anything else that is pleasant to drink ;
   Mix sand with the cider, and wool with the wine —
   And welcome Queen Alice with ninety-times-nine ! "

" Ninety times nine ! " Alice repeated in despair.
" Oh, that'll never be done ! I'd better go in at
once ; " and in she went, and there was a dead silence
the moment she appeared.

Alice glanced nervously along the table, as she
walked up the large hall, and noticed that there were
about fifty guests of all kinds ; some were animals,
some birds, and there were even a few flowers among
them. " I'm glad they've come without waiting to be
asked," she thought; " I should never have known
who were the right people to invite ! "

There were three chairs at the head of the table ;
the Red and White Queens had already taken two of
them, but the middle one was empty. Alice sat down
in it, rather uncomfortable at the silence, and longing
for some one to speak.

At last the Red Queen began. " You've missed
the soup and fish," she said. " Put on the joint ! "
And the waiters set a leg of mutton before Alice, who
looked at it rather anxiously, as she never had to carve
a joint before.

" You look a little shy ; let me introduce you to that

leg of mutton," said the Red Queen. "Alice — Mut‸ton; Mutton — Alice." The leg of mutton got up in the dish and made a little bow to Alice; and Alice returned the bow, not knowing whether to be frightened or amused.

"May I give you a slice?" she said, taking up the knife and fork, and looking from one Queen to the other.

"Certainly not," the Red Queen said, very decidedly: "it isn't etiquette to cut any one you've been introduced to. Remove the joint!" And the waiters carried it off, and brought a large plum-pudding in its place.

"I won't be introduced to the pudding, please," Alice said, rather hastily, "or we shall get no dinner at all. May I give you some?"

But the Red Queen looked sulky, and growled "Pudding — Alice; Alice — Pudding. Remove the pudding!" and the waiters took it away so quickly that Alice couldn't return its bow.

However, she didn't see why the Red Queen should be the only one to give orders, so, as an experiment, she called out, "Waiter! Bring back the pudding!" and there it was again in a moment, like a conjuring-trick! It was so large that she couldn't help feeling a *little* shy with it, as she had been with the mutton; however, she conquered her shyness by a great effort, and cut a slice and handed it to the Red Queen.

"What impertinence!" said the Pudding. "I won-

der how you'd like it, if I were to cut a slice out of *you*,
you creature!"

It spoke in a thick, suety sort of a voice, and Alice
hadn't a word to say in reply: she could only sit and
look at it and gasp.

"Make a remark," said the Red Queen: "it's
ridiculous to leave all the conversation to the pudding!"

"Do you know, I've had such a quantity of poetry
repeated to me to-day," Alice began, a little frightened
at finding that, the moment she opened her lips, there
was dead silence, and all eyes were fixed upon her;
"and it's a very curious thing, I think — every poem
was about fishes in some way. Do you know why
they're so fond of fishes, all about here?"

She spoke to the Red Queen, whose answer was a
little wide of the mark. "As to fishes," she said,
very slowly and solemnly, putting her mouth close to
Alice's ear, "her White Majesty knows a lovely riddle
— all in poetry — all about fishes. Shall she repeat
it?"

"Her Red Majesty's very kind to mention it," the
White Queen murmured into Alice's other ear, in a
voice like the cooing of a pigeon. "It would be *such*
a treat! May I?"

"Please do," Alice said, very politely.

The White Queen laughed with delight, and stroked
Alice's cheek. Then she began:

"'First, the fish must be caught.'
That is easy: a baby, I think, could have caught it.
'Next, the fish must be bought.'
That is easy: a penny, I think, would have bought it.

'Now cook me the fish!'
That is easy, and will not take more than a minute.
'Let it lie in a dish!'
That is easy, because it already is in it.

'Bring it here!   Let me sup!'
It is easy, to set such a dish on the table.
'Take the dish-cover up!'
Ah, that is so hard that I fear I'm unable!

For it holds it like glue —
Holds the lid to the dish, while it lies in the middle:
Which is easiest to do,
Un-dish-cover the fish, or dishcover the riddle?"

"Take a minute to think about it, and then guess,"
said the Red Queen.   "Meanwhile, we'll drink your
health — Queen Alice's health!" she screamed at the
top of her voice, and all the guests began drinking it
directly, and very queerly they managed it; some of
them put their glasses upon their heads like extinguish-
ers, and drank all that trickled down their faces —
others upset the decanters, and drank the wine as it
ran off the edges of the table — and three of them (who
looked like kangaroos) scrambled into the dish of roast
mutton, and began eagerly lapping up the gravy, "just
like pigs in a trough!" thought Alice.

"You ought to return thanks in a neat speech," the
Red Queen said, frowning at Alice as she spoke.

"We must support you, you know," the White Queen
whispered, as Alice got up to do it, very obediently, but
a little frightened.

"Thank you very much," she whispered in reply,
" but I can do quite well without."

"That wouldn't be at all the thing," the Red Queen

said very decidedly; so Alice tried to submit to it with a good grace.

("And they *did* push so!" she said afterward, when she was telling her sister the history of the feast. "You would have thought they wanted to squeeze me flat!")

In fact it was rather difficult for her to keep in her place while she made her speech; the two Queens pushed her so, one on each side, that they nearly lifted her up into the air. "I rise to return thanks —— " Alice began; and she really *did* rise as she spoke, several inches; but she got hold of the edge of the table, and managed to pull herself down again.

"Take care of yourself!" screamed the White Queen, seizing Alice's hair with both her hands. "Something's going to happen!"

And then (as Alice afterward described it) all sorts

of things happened in a moment. The candles all grew up to the ceiling, looking something like a bed of rushes with fireworks at the top. As to the bottles, they each took a pair of plates, which they hastily fitted on as wings, and so, with forks for legs, went fluttering about in all directions; "and very like birds they look," Alice thought to herself, as well as she could in the dreadful confusion that was beginning.

At this moment she heard a hoarse laugh at her side, and turned to see what was the matter with the White Queen, but instead of the Queen there was the leg of mutton sitting in the chair. " Here I am ! " cried a voice from the soup-tureen, and Alice turned again, just in time to see the Queen's broad, good-natured face grinning at her for a moment over the edge of the tureen, before she disappeared into the soup.

There was not a moment to be lost. Already several of the guests were lying down in the dishes, and the soup-ladle was walking up the table toward Alice's chair, and beckoning to her impatiently to get out of its way.

" I can't stand this any longer ! " she cried as she jumped up and seized the table-cloth with both hands ; one good pull, and plates, dishes, guests, and candles came crashing down together in a heap on the floor.

A RUSTIC DRAMA

(FROM A MIDSUMMER-NIGHT'S DREAM.)

BY WILLIAM SHAKESPEARE.

SCENE I. *Athens.* QUINCE'S *house.*

Enter QUINCE, SNUG, BOTTOM, FLUTE, SNOUT, *and* STARVELING.

QUINCE. Is all our company here?

Bottom. You were best to call them generally, man by man, according to the scrip.

Quince. Here is the scroll of every man's name, which is thought fit, through all Athens, to play in our interlude before the duke and the duchess, on his wedding-day at night.

Bottom. First, good Peter Quince, say what the play treats on, then read the names of the actors, and so grow to a point.

Quince. Marry, our play is, The most lamentable comedy, and most cruel death of Pyramus and Thisby.

Bottom. A very good piece of work, I assure you,

and a merry. Now, good Peter Quince, call forth your actors by the scroll. Masters, spread yourselves.

Quince. Answer as I call you. Nick Bottom, the weaver.

Bottom. Ready. Name what part I am for, and proceed.

Quince. You, Nick Bottom, are set down for Pyramus.

Bottom. What is Pyramus? a lover, or a tyrant?

Quince. A lover, that kills himself most gallant for love.

Bottom. That will ask some tears in the true performing of it: if I do it, let the audience look to their eyes; I will move storms, I will condole in some measure. To the rest: yet my chief humor is for a tyrant: I could play Ercles rarely, or a part to tear a cat in, to make all split.

> The raging rocks
> And shivering shocks
> Shall break the locks
>   Of prison gates;
> And Phibbus' car
> Shall shine from far
> And make and mar
>   The foolish Fates.

This was lofty! Now name the rest of the players. This is Ercles' vein, a tyrant's vein; a lover is more condoling.

Quince. Francis Flute, the bellows-mender.

Flute. Here, Peter Quince.

Quince. Flute, you must take Thisby on you.

Flute. What is Thisby? a wandering knight?

Quince. It is the lady that Pyramus must love.

Flute. Nay, faith, let not me play a woman; I have a beard coming.

Quince. That's all one; you shall play it in a mask, and you may speak as small as you will.

Bottom. An I may hide my face, let me play Thisby too, I'll speak in a monstrous little voice, "Thisne, Thisne;" "Ah Pyramus, my lover dear! thy Thisby dear, and lady dear!"

Quince. No, no; you must play Pyramus: and, Flute, you Thisby.

Bottom. Well, proceed.

Quince. Robin Starveling, the tailor.

Starveling. Here, Peter Quince.

Quince. Robin Starveling, you must play Thisby's mother. Tom Snout, the tinker.

Snout. Here, Peter Quince.

Quince. You, Pyramus' father: myself, Thisby's father. Snug, the joiner; you, the lion's part: and, I hope, here is a play fitted.

Snug. Have you the lion's part written? pray you, if it be, give it me, for I am slow of study.

Quince. You may do it extempore, for it is nothing but roaring.

Bottom. Let me play the lion too: I will roar, that I will do any man's heart good to hear me; I will roar, that I will make the duke say "Let him roar again, let him roar again."

Quince. An you should do it too terribly, you would fright the duchess and the ladies, that they would shriek; and that were enough to hang us all.

All. That would hang us, every mother's son.

II-6

Bottom. I grant you, friends, if that you should fright the ladies out of their wits, they would have no more discretion but to hang us : but I will aggravate my voice so that I will roar you as gently as any sucking dove ; I will roar you an 'twere any nightingale.

Quince. You can play no part but Pyramus ; for Pyramus is a sweet-faced man ; a proper man, as one shall see in a summer's day ; a most lovely gentleman-like man : therefore you must needs play Pyramus.

Bottom. Well, I will undertake it. What beard were I best to play it in?

Quince. Why, what you will.

Bottom. I will discharge it in either your straw-color beard, your orange-tawny beard, your purple-in-grain beard, or your French-crown-color beard, your perfect yellow.

Quince. Some of your French crowns have no hair at all, and then you will play barefaced. But, masters, here are your parts : and I am to entreat you, request you and desire you, to con them by to-morrow night ; and meet me in the palace-wood, a mile without the town, by moonlight ; there will we rehearse, for if we meet in the city, we shall be dogged with company, and our devices known. In the meantime I will draw a bill of properties, such as our play wants. I pray you, fail me not.

Bottom. We will meet ; and there we may rehearse most obscenely and courageously. Take pains ; be perfect : adieu.

Quince. At the duke's oak we meet.

Bottom. Enough ; hold or cut bow-strings.

Exeunt.

SCENE II. *The wood. Titania lying asleep.*

Enter QUINCE, SNUG, BOTTOM, FLUTE, SNOUT, *and*
STARVELING.

Bottom.   Are we all met?

Quince.   Pat, pat; and here's a marvellous convenient place for our rehearsal. This green plot shall be
our stage, this hawthorn-brake our tiring-house; and we
will do it in action as we will do it before the duke.

Bottom.   Peter Quince, —

Quince.   What sayest thou, Bully Bottom?

Bottom.   There are things in this comedy of Pyramus and Thisby that will never please. First, Pyramus
must draw a sword to kill himself; which the ladies
cannot abide. How answer you that?

Snout.   By'r lakin, a parlous fear.

Starveling.   I believe we must leave the killing out,
when all is done.

Bottom.   Not a whit: I have a device to make all
well. Write me a prologue; and let the prologue seem
to say, we will do no harm with our swords and that
Pyramus is not killed indeed; and, for the more better
assurance, tell them that I Pyramus am not Pyramus,
but Bottom the weaver: this will put them out of fear.

Quince.   Well, we will have such a prologue; and it
shall be written in eight and six.

Bottom.   No, make it two more; let it be written in
eight and eight.

Snout.   Will not the ladies be afeard of the lion?

Starveling.   I fear it, I promise you.

Bottom.   Masters, you ought to consider with your-

selves: to bring in — God shield us! — a lion among
ladies, is a most dreadful thing; for there is not a more
fearful wild-fowl than your lion living; and we ought
to look to 't.

Snout. Therefore another prologue must tell he is
not a lion.

Bottom. Nay, you must name his name, and half
his face must be seen through the lion's neck: and he
himself must speak through, saying thus, or to the same
defect, — " Ladies," — or " Fair ladies, — I would wish
you," — or " I would request you," — or " I would entreat you, — not to fear, not to tremble: my life for
yours. If you think I come hither as a lion, it were
pity of my life: no, I am no such thing; I am a man
as other men are; " and there indeed let him name his
name, and tell them plainly he is Snug the joiner.

Quince. Well, it shall be so. But there is two hard
things; that is, to bring the moonlight into a chamber;
for, you know, Pyramus and Thisby meet by moonlight.

Snout. Doth the moon shine that night we play our
play?

Bottom. A calendar, a calendar! look in the alma-
nac; find out moonshine, find out moonshine.

Quince. Yes, it doth shine that night.

Bottom. Why, then you may leave a casement of
the great chamber window, where we play, open, and
the moon may shine in at the casement.

Quince. Ay; or else one must come in with a bush
of thorns and a lanthorn, and say he comes to disfigure,
or to present, the person of Moonshine. Then, there
is another thing: we must have a wall in the great

chamber; for Pyramus and Thisby, says the story, did talk through the chink of a wall.

Snout. You can never bring in a wall. What say you, Bottom?

Bottom. Some man or other must present Wall: and let him have some plaster, or some loam, or some rough-cast about him, to signify wall; and let him hold his fingers thus, and through that cranny shall Pyramus and Thisby whisper.

Quince. If that may be, then all is well. Come, sit down, every mother's son, and rehearse your parts. Pyramus, you begin: when you have spoken your speech, enter into that brake: and so every one according to his cue.

Enter PUCK *behind.*

Puck. What hempen homespuns have we swaggering here,
So near the cradle of the fairy queen?
What, a play toward! I'll be an auditor;
An actor too perhaps, if I see cause.

Quince. Speak, Pyramus. Thisby, stand forth.

Bottom. Thisby, the flowers of odious savors sweet, ——

Quince. Odors, odors.

Bottom. —— odors savors sweet:
So hath thy breath, my dearest Thisby dear.
But hark, a voice! stay thou but here awhile,
And by and by I will to thee appear.   [*Exit.*

Puck. A stranger Pyramus than e'er played here.
          [*Exit.*

Flute. Must I speak now?

Quince. Ay, marry, must you; for you must understand he goes but to see a noise that he heard, and is to come again.

Flute. Most radiant Pyramus, most lily white of
      hue,
Of color like the red rose on triumphant brier,
Most brisky juvenal and eke most lovely Jew,
   As true as truest horse that yet would never tire,
I'll meet thee, Pyramus, at Ninny's tomb.

Quince. "Ninus' tomb," man: why, you must not speak that yet; that you answer to Pyramus: you speak all your part at once, cues and all. Pyramus enter: your cue is past; it is, "never tire."

Flute. O, — As true as truest horse, that yet would
      never tire.

Re-enter PUCK, *and* BOTTOM *with an ass's head.*

Bottom. If I were fair, Thisby, I were only thine.

Quince. O monstrous! O strange! we are haunted. Pray, masters! fly, masters! Help!

      [*Exeunt* QUINCE, SNUG, FLUTE, SNOUT, *and*
            STARVELING.

Puck. I'll follow you, I'll lead you about a round,
   Through bog, through bush, through brake, through
      brier:
Sometime a horse I'll be, sometime a hound,
   A hog, a headless bear, sometime a fire;
And neigh, and bark, and grunt, and roar, and burn,
Like horse, hound, hog, bear, fire, at every turn.

                                          [*Exit.*

Bottom. Why do they run away? this is a knavery of them to make me afeard.

Re-enter SNOUT.

Snout. O Bottom, thou art changed! what do I
see on thee?

Bottom. What do you see? you see an ass-head of
your own, do you?   [*Exit Snout.*

Re-enter QUINCE.

Quince. Bless thee, Bottom! bless thee! thou art
translated.   [*Exit.*

Bottom. I see their knavery: this is to make an ass
of me; to fright me, if they could. But I will not stir
from this place, do what they can: I will walk up and
down here, and I will sing, that they shall hear I am
not afraid.   [*Sings.*

> The ousel cock so black of hue,
>   With orange-tawny bill,
> The throstle with his note so true,
>   The wren with little quill, —

Titania [*awaking*]. What angel wakes me from my
flowery bed?

Bottom [*sings*].

> The finch, the sparrow, and the lark,
>   The plain-song cuckoo gray,
> Whose note full many a man doth mark,
>   And dares not answer nay; —

for, indeed, who would set his wit to so foolish a bird?
who would give a bird the lie, though he cry " cuckoo "
never so?

Titania. I pray thee, gentle mortal, sing again:
Mine ear is much enamoured of thy note;
So is mine eye enthralled to thy shape;

And thy fair virtue's force perforce doth move me
On the first view to say, to swear, I love thee.

Bottom. Methinks, mistress, you should have little reason for that: and yet, to say the truth, reason and

love keep little company together now-a-days; the more the pity that some honest neighbors will not make them friends. Nay, I can gleek upon occasion.

Titania. Thou art as wise as thou art beautiful.

Bottom. Not so, neither; but if I had wit

Titania. "Thou art as Wise as Thou art Beautiful."

enough to get out of this wood, I have enough to serve mine own turn.

Titania. Out of this wood do not desire to go:
Thou shalt remain here, whether thou wilt or no.
I am a spirit of no common rate:
The summer still doth tend upon my state;
And I do love thee: therefore, go with me;
I'll give thee fairies to attend on thee,
And they shall fetch thee jewels from the deep,
And sing while thou on pressed flowers dost sleep:

And I will purge thy mortal grossness so
That thou shalt like an airy spirit go.
Peaseblossom! Cobweb! Moth! and Mustardseed!

Enter PEASEBLOSSOM, COBWEB, MOTH *and*
MUSTARDSEED.

Peaseblossom. Ready.
Cobweb.   And I.
Moth.   And I.
Mustardseed.   And I.
All.   Where shall we go?
Titania.   Be kind and courteous to this gentleman;
Hop in his walks and gambol in his eyes;
Feed him with apricocks and dewberries,
With purple grapes, green figs, and mulberries;
The honey-bags steal from the bumble-bees,
And for night-tapers crop their waxen thighs
And light them at the fiery glow-worm's eyes,
To have my love to bed and to arise;
And pluck the wings from painted butterflies
To fan the moonbeams from his sleeping eyes:
Nod to him, elves, and do him courtesies.
Peaseblossom. Hail, mortal!
Cobweb. Hail!
Moth. Hail!
Mustardseed. Hail!
Bottom. I cry your worships mercy, heartily: I be-
seech your worship's name.
Cobweb. Cobweb.
Bottom. I shall desire you of more acquaintance,
good Master Cobweb: if I cut my finger, I shall make
bold with you. Your name, honest gentleman?

Peaseblossom.   Peaseblossom.

Bottom.   I pray you, commend me to Mistress
Squash, your mother, and to Master Peascod, your
father.   Good Master Peaseblossom, I shall desire you
of more acquaintance too.   Your name, I beseech you,
sir?

Mustardseed.   Mustardseed.

Bottom.   Good Master Mustardseed, I know your
patience well: that same cowardly, giant-like ox-beef
hath devoured many a gentleman of your house: I
promise you your kindred hath made my eyes water ere
now.   I desire your more acquaintance, good Master
Mustardseed.

Titania.   Come, wait upon him; lead him to my
bower.

SCENE III.   *The Wood.*

Bottom [*awaking*].   When my cue comes, call me,
and I will answer: my next is, "Most fair Pyramus."
Heigh-ho!   Peter Quince!   Flute, the bellows-mender!
Snout, the tinker!   Starveling!   God's my life, stolen
hence, and left me asleep!   I have had a most rare
vision.   I have had a dream, past the wit of man to
say what dream it was: man is but an ass, if he go
about to expound this dream.   Methought I was —
there is no man can tell what.   Methought I was, —
and methought I had, — but man is but a patched fool,
if he will offer to say what methought I had.   The eye
of man hath not heard, the ear of man hath not seen,
man's hand is not able to taste, his tongue to conceive,
nor his heart to report, what my dream was.   I will
get Peter Quince to write a ballad of this dream: it

shall be called Bottom's Dream, because it hath no bottom; and I will sing it in the latter end of a play, before the duke: peradventure, to make it the more gracious, I shall sing it at her death.   [*Exit.*

Scene IV. *Athens.* Quince's *house.*

Enter Quince, Flute, Snout, *and* Starveling.

Quince. Have you sent to Bottom's house? is he come home yet?

Starveling. He cannot be heard of.   Out of doubt he is transported.

Flute. If he come not, then the play is marred: it goes not forward, doth it?

Quince. It is not possible: you have not a man in all Athens able to discharge Pyramus but he.

Flute. No, he hath simply the best wit of any handicraft man in Athens.

Quince. Yea, and the best person too; and he is a very paramour for a sweet voice.

Flute. You must say " paragon: " a paramour is, God bless us, a thing of naught.

Enter Snug.

Snug. Masters, the duke is coming from the temple, and there is two or three lords and ladies more married: if our sport had gone forward, we had all been made men.

Flute. O sweet bully Bottom! Thus hath he lost sixpence a day during his life; he could not have 'scaped sixpence a day: an the duke had not given him sixpence a day for playing Pyramus, I'll be hanged ; he would have deserved it : sixpence a day in Pyramus, or nothing.

Enter BOTTOM.

Bottom. Where are these lads? where are these hearts ?

Quince. Bottom ! O most courageous day ! O most happy hour !

Bottom. Masters, I am to discourse wonders : but ask me not what ; for if I tell you, I am no true Athenian. I will tell you every thing, right as it fell out.

Quince. Let us hear, sweet Bottom.

Bottom. Not a word of me. All that I will tell you is, that the duke hath dined. Get your apparel together, good strings to your beards, new ribbons to your pumps ; meet presently at the palace ; every man look o'er his part ; for the short and the long is, our play is preferred. In any case, let Thisby have clean linen ; and let not him that plays the lion pare his nails, for they shall hang out for the lion's claws. And, most dear actors, eat no onions nor garlic, for we are to utter sweet breath ; and I do not doubt but to hear them say, it is a sweet comedy. No more words : away ! go, away !   [*Exeunt.*

SCENE V.   *Athens.   The palace of* THESEUS.

THESEUS, HIPPOLYTA, PHILOSTRATE, LYSANDER, DEME-TRIUS, HERMINA, HELENA, Lords, *and* Attendants.

Theseus. Come now ; what masques, what dances shall we have,
To wear away this long age of three hours

Between our after-supper and bed-time?
Where is our usual manager of mirth?
What revels are in hand? Is there no play,
To ease the anguish of a torturing hour?
Call Philostrate.

 Philostrate. Here, mighty Theseus.

 Theseus. Say, what abridgement have you for this
  evening?

What masque? what music? How shall we beguile
The lazy time, if not with some delight?

 Philostrate. There is a brief how many sports are ripe:
Make choice of which your highness will see first.

          [Giving a paper.

 Theseus [reads]. " The battle with the Centaurs, to
  be sung
By an Athenian eunuch to the harp."
We'll none of that: that have I told my love,
In glory of my kinsman Hercules.

[*Reads.*] " The riot of the tipsy Bacchanals,
Tearing the Thracian singer in their rage."
That is an old device; and it was played
When I from Thebes came last a conqueror.

[*Reads.*] " The thrice three Muses mourning for the
  death
Of Learning, late deceased in beggary."
That is some satire, keen and critical,
Not sorting with a nuptial ceremony.

[*Reads.*] " A tedious brief scene of young Pyramus
And his love Thisby; very tragical mirth."
Merry and tragical! tedious and brief!
That is, hot ice and wondrous strange snow.
How shall we find the concord of this discord?

Philostrate. A play there is, my lord, some ten words
    long,
Which is as brief as I have known a play;
But by ten words, my lord, it is too long,
Which makes it tedious; for in all the play
There is not one word apt, one play fitted:
And tragical, my noble lord, it is;
For Pyramus therein doth kill himself.
Which, when I saw rehearsed, I must confess,
Made mine eyes water; but more merry tears
The passion of loud laughter never shed.
    Theseus. What are they that do play it?
    Philostrate. Hard-handed men that work in Athens
    here,
Which never labored in their minds till now,
And now have toiled their unbreathed memories
With this same play, against your nuptial.
    Theseus. And we will hear it.
    Philostrate.   No, my noble lord;
It is not for you: I have heard it over,
And it is nothing, nothing in the world;
Unless you can find sport in their intents,
Extremely stretched and conned with cruel pain,
To do you service.
    Theseus.   I will hear that play;
For never anything can be amiss,
When simpleness and duty tender it.
Go, bring them in: and take your places, ladies.
                      [*Exit Philostrate.*
    Hippolyta. I love not to see wretchedness o'ercharged
And duty in his service perishing.
    Theseus. Why, gentle sweet, you shall see no such
    thing.

Hippolyta. He says they can do nothing in this kind.

Theseus. The kinder we, to give them thanks for
   nothing.

Our sport shall be to take what they mistake:

And what poor duty cannot do, noble respect

Takes it in might, not merit.

Where I have come, great clerks have purposed

To greet me with premeditated welcomes;

Where I have seen them shiver and look pale,

Make periods in the midst of sentences,

Throttle their practised accent in their fears

And in conclusion dumbly have broke off,

Not paying me a welcome. Trust me, sweet,

Out of this silence yet I picked a welcome;

And in the modesty of fearful duty

I read as much as from the rattling tongue

Of saucy and audacious eloquence.

Love, therefore, and tongue-tied simplicity

In least speak most, to my capacity.

Re-enter PHILOSTRATE.

Philostrate. So please your grace, the Prologue is
   addressed.

Theseus. Let him approach. [*Flourish of trumpets.*

Enter QUINCE *for the* Prologue.

Prologue. If we offend, it is with our good will.

   That you should think, we come not to offend,

But with good will. To show our simple skill,

   That is the true beginning of our end.

Consider then we come but in despite.

We do not come as minding to content you,

Our true intent is.   All for your delight
   We are not here.   That you should here repent you,
The actors are at hand and by their show
You shall know all that you are like to know.

Theseus.   This fellow doth not stand upon points.

Lysander.   He hath rid his prologue like a rough colt;
he knows not the stop.   A good moral, my lord : it is
not enough to speak, but to speak true.

Hippolyta.   Indeed he hath played on his prologue
like a child on a recorder ; a sound, but not in government.

Theseus.   His speech was like a tangled chain; nothing impaired, but all disordered.   Who is next?

Enter PYRAMUS *and* THISBY, WALL, MOON, *and* LION.

Prologue.   Gentles, perchance you wonder at this
      show ;
   But wonder on, till truth make all things plain.
This man is Pyramus, if you would know ;
   This beauteous lady Thisby is certain.
This man, with lime and rough-cast, doth present
   Wall, that vile Wall which did these lovers sunder ;
And through Wall's chink, poor souls, they are content
   To whisper.   At the which let no man wonder.
This man, with lanthorn, dog, and bush of thorn,
   Presenteth Moonshine ; for, if you will know,
By moonshine did these lovers think no scorn
   To meet at Ninus' tomb, there, there to woo.
This grisly beast, which Lion hight by name,
   The trusty Thisby, coming first by night,
Did scare away. or rather did affright ;

And, as she fled, her mantle she did fall,
  Which Lion vile with bloody mouth did stain.
Anon comes Pyramus, sweet youth and tall,
  And finds his trusty Thisby's mantle slain:
Whereat, with blade, with bloody blameful blade,
  He bravely broach'd his boiling bloody breast;
And Thisby, tarrying in mulberry shade,
  His dagger drew, and died.   For
    all the rest,
Let Lion, Moonshine, Wall, and
    lovers twain
At large discourse, while here they
    do remain.
[*Exeunt Prologue, Pyramus, Thisby,*
    Lion, and Moon.
  Theseus. I wonder if the lion be
    to speak.
  Demetrius. No wonder, my lord:
one lion may, when many asses do.
  Wall. In this same interlude it
    doth befall

PYRAMUS.

That I, one Snout by name, pre-
    sent a wall;
And such a wall, as I would have
    you think,
That had in it a crannied hole or chink,
Through which the lovers, Pyramus and Thisby,
Did whisper often very secretly.
This loam, this rough-cast and this stone doth show
That I am that same wall; the truth is so:
And this the cranny is, right and sinister,
Through which the fearful lovers are to whisper.

Theseus. Would you desire lime and hair to speak better?

Demetrius. It is the wittiest partition that ever I heard discourse, my lord.

Re-enter PYRAMUS.

Theseus. Pyramus draws near the wall: silence!

Pyramus. O grim-looked night! O night with hue
    so black!
O night, which ever art when day is not!
O night, O night! alack, alack, alack,
    I fear my Thisby's promise is forgot!
And thou, O wall, O sweet, O lovely wall,
    That stand'st between her father's ground and mine!
Thou wall, O wall, O sweet and lovely wall,
    Show me thy chink, to blink through with mine eyne!
        [*Wall holds up his fingers.*
Thanks, courteous wall: Jove shield thee well for this!
    But what see I? No Thisby do I see.
O wicked wall, through whom I see no bliss!
    Cursed be thy stones for thus deceiving me!

Theseus. The wall, methinks, being sensible, should curse again.

Pyramus. No, in truth, sir, he should not. "Deceiving me" is Thisby's cue: she is to enter now, and I am to spy her through the wall. You shall see, it will fall pat as I told you. Yonder she comes.

Re-enter THISBY.

Thisby. O wall, full often hast thou heard my moans,
    For parting my fair Pyramus and me!
My cherry lips have often kissed thy stones,
    Thy stones with lime and hair knit up in thee.

Pyramus. I see a voice: now will I to the chink,
To spy an I can hear my Thisby's face.
Thisby!

Thisby. My love thou art, my love I think.

Pyramus. Think what thou wilt, I am thy lover's
grace:
And, like Limander, am I trusty still.

Thisby. And I like Helen, till the Fates me kill.

Pyramus. Not Shafalus to Procrus was so true.

Thisby. As Shafalus to Procrus, I to you.

Pyramus. O, kiss me through the hole of this vile
wall!

Thisby. I kiss the wall's hole, not your lips at all.

Pyramus. Wilt thou at Ninny's tomb meet me
straightway?

Thisby. 'Tide life, 'tide death, I come without delay.

[Exeunt Pyramus and Thisby.

Wall. Thus have I, Wall, my part discharged so;
And being done, thus Wall away doth go. *[Exit.*

Theseus. Now is the mural down between the two
neighbors.

Demetrius. No remedy, my lord, when walls are so
wilful to hear without warning.

Hippolyta. This is the silliest stuff that ever I
heard.

Theseus. The best in this kind are but shadows; and
the worst are no worse, if imagination amend them.

Hippolyta. It must be your imagination then, and
not theirs.

Theseus. If we imagine no worse of them than they
of themselves, they may pass for excellent men. Here
come two noble beasts in, a man and a lion.

Re-enter LION *and* MOON.

Lion. You, ladies, you, whose gentle hearts do fear
  The smallest monstrous mouse that creeps on floor,
May now perchance both quake and tremble here,
  When lion rough in wildest rage doth roar.
Then know that I, one Snug the joiner, am
A lion-fell, nor else no lion's dam;
For, if I should as lion come in strife
Into this place, 'twere pity on my life.

Theseus. A very gentle beast, and of a good conscience.

Demetrius. The very best at a beast, my lord, that e'er I saw.

Lysander. This lion is a very fox for his valor.

Theseus. True; and a goose for his discretion.

Demetrius. Not so, my lord; for his valor cannot carry his discretion; and the fox carries the goose.

Theseus. His discretion, I am sure, cannot carry his valor; for the goose carries not the fox. It is well: leave it to his discretion, and let us listen to the moon.

Moon. This lanthorn doth the horned moon present; —

Demetrius. He should have worn the horns on his head.

Theseus. He is no crescent, and his horns are invisble within the circumference.

Moon. This lanthorn doth the horned moon present; Myself the man i' the moon do seem to be.

Theseus. This is the greatest error of all the rest: the man should be put into the lanthorn. How is it else the man i' the moon?

Demetrius. He dares not come there for the candle; for, you see, it is already in snuff.

Hippolyta. I am aweary of this moon: would he would change!

Theseus. It appears, by his small light of discretion, that he is in the wane; but yet, in courtesy, in all reason, we must stay the time.

Lysander. Proceed, Moon.

Moon. All that I have to say, is, to tell you that the lanthorn is the moon; I, the man in the moon; this thorn-bush, my thorn-bush; and this dog, my dog.

Demetrius. Why, all these should be in the lanthorn; for all these are in the moon. But, silence! here comes Thisby.

Re-enter THISBY.

Thisby. This is old Ninny's tomb. Where is my love?

Lion [*roaring*]. Oh — [*Thisby runs off.*

Demetrius. Well roared, Lion.

Theseus. Well run, Thisby.

Hippolyta. Well shone, Moon. Truly, the moon shines with a good grace.

[*The Lion shakes Thisby's Mantle, and exit.*

Theseus. Well moused, Lion.

Lysander. And so the lion vanished.

Demetrius. And then came Pyramus.

Re-enter Pyramus.

Pyramus. Sweet Moon, I thank thee for thy sunny beams;

I thank thee, Moon, for shining now so bright;

For, by thy gracious, golden, glittering gleams,
   I trust to take of truest Thisby sight.
            But stay, O spite!
            But mark, poor knight,
       What dreadful dole is here!
         Eyes, do you see?
         How can it be.?
       O dainty duck! O dear!
        Thy mantle good,
      What, stain'd with blood!
     Approach, ye Furies fell!
       O Fates, come, come,
       Cut thread and thrum;
   Quail, crush, conclude, and quell!

Theseus. This passion, and the death of a dear
friend, would go near to make a man look sad.

Hippolyta. Beshrew my heart, but I pity the man.

Pyramus. O wherefore, Nature, didst thou lions
      frame?

Since lion vile hath here deflowered my dear:

Which is — no, no — which was the fairest dame

That lived, that loved, that liked, that looked with cheer.
       Come, tears, confound;
       Out, sword, and wound
      The pap of Pyramus;
       Ay, that left pap,
      Where heart doth hop: [*Stabs himself.*

Thus die I, thus, thus, thus.
        Now am I dead,
        Now am I fled;
      My soul is in the sky:
      Tongue, lose thy light;

Moon, take thy flight: [*Exit Moon.*
Now die, die, die, die, die.   [*Dies.*

Demetrius. No die, but an ace, for him; for he is but one.

Lysander. Less than an ace, man; for he is dead; he is nothing.

Theseus. With the help of a surgeon he might yet recover, and prove an ass.

Hippolyta. How chance Moonshine is gone before Thisby comes back and finds her lover?

Theseus. She will find him by starlight. Here she comes; and her passion ends the play.

Re-enter THISBY.

Hippolyta. Methinks she should not use a long one for such a Pyramus: I hope she will be brief.

Demetrius. A mote will turn the balance, which Pyramus, which Thisby, is the better; he for a man, God warrant us; she for a woman, God bless us.

Lysander. She hath spied him already with those sweet eyes.

Demetrius. And thus she means, videlicet —:

Thisby.   Asleep, my love?
    What, dead, my dove?
   O Pyramus, arise!
    Speak, speak. Quite dumb?
    Dead, dead? A tomb
   Must cover thy sweet eyes.
    These lily lips,
    This cherry nose,
   These yellow cowslip cheeks,
    Are gone, are gone:

"Thus Thisby Ends."

Lovers, make moan:
His eyes were green as leeks.
O Sisters Three,
Come, come to me,
With hands as pale as milk;
Lay them in gore,
Since you have shore
With shears his thread of silk.
Tongue, not a word:
Come, trusty sword;
Come, blade, my breast imbrue: *[Stabs herself.*
And, farewell, friends;
Thus Thisby ends:
Adieu, adieu, adieu. *[Dies.*

Theseus. Moonshine and Lion are left to bury the dead.

Demetrius. Ay, and Wall too.

Bottom [starting up]. No, I assure you; the wall is down that parted their fathers. Will it please you to see the epilogue, or to hear a Bergomask dance between two of our company?

Theseus. No epilogue, I pray you; for your play needs no excuse. Never excuse; for when the players are all dead, there need none to be blamed. Marry, if he that writ it had played Pyramus and hanged himself in Thisby's garter, it would have been a fine tragedy: and so it is truly; and very notably discharged. But, come, your Bergomask: let your epilogue alone.

[A dance.

The iron tongue of midnight hath told twelve:
Lovers, to bed; 'tis almost fairy time.

I fear we shall out-sleep the coming morn
As much as we this night have overwatched.
This palpable-gross play hath well beguiled
The heavy gait of night.   Sweet friends, to bed.
A fortnight hold we this solemnity,
In nightly revels and new jollity.

THE KNIGHT

(From Through The Looking-Glass.)

By LEWIS CARROLL.

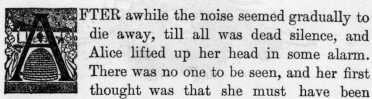

FTER awhile the noise seemed gradually to die away, till all was dead silence, and Alice lifted up her head in some alarm. There was no one to be seen, and her first thought was that she must have been dreaming about the Lion and the Unicorn and those queer Anglo-Saxon Messengers. However, there was the great dish still lying at her feet, on which she had tried to cut the plum-cake. "So I wasn't dreaming after all," she said to herself, "unless — unless we're all part of the same dream. Only I do hope it's *my* dream, and not the Red King's. I don't like belonging to another person's dream," she went on in a rather complaining tone: " I've a great mind to go and wake him, and see what happens."

At this moment her thoughts were interrupted by a loud shouting of "Ahoy! Ahoy! Check!" and a Knight, dressed in crimson armor, came galloping down upon her, brandishing a great club. Just as he reached her, the horse stopped suddenly: "You're my prisoner," the Knight cried, as he tumbled off his horse.

Startled as she was, Alice was more frightened for
him than for herself at the moment, and watched him
with some anxiety as he mounted again. As soon as
he was comfortably in the saddle, he began once more,
" You're my —— " but here another voice broke in,
" Ahoy! Ahoy! Check," and Alice looked round in
some surprise for the new enemy.

This time it was a White Knight. He drew up at
Alice's side, and tumbled off his horse just as the Red
Knight had done : then
he got on again, and
the two Knights sat
and looked at each
other for some
t i m e without
speaking. Alice
looked from one
to the other in
some bewilder-
ment.

" She's *my*
prisoner, you
know!" the Red
Knight said at
last.

" Yes, but then *I* came and rescued her!" the White
Knight replied.

" Well, we must fight for her then," said the Red
Knight, as he took up his helmet (which hung from the
saddle, and was something the shape of a horse's head),
and put it on.

" You will observe the Rules of Battle, of course ? "

the White Knight remarked, putting on his helmet too.

"I always do," said the Red Knight, and they began banging away at each other with such fury that Alice got behind a tree to be out of the way of the blows.

"I wonder, now, what the Rules of Battle are," she said to herself, as she watched the fight, timidly peeping out from her hiding-place: "one Rule seems to be, that if one Knight hits the other, he knocks him off his horse, and if he misses, he tumbles off himself — and another Rule seems to be that they hold their clubs with their arms, as if they were Punch and Judy. What a noise they make when they tumble! Just like a whole set of fire-irons falling into the fender! And how quiet the horses are! They let them get on and off them just as if they were tables!"

Another Rule of Battle, that Alice had not noticed, seemed to be that they always fell on their heads, and the battle ended with their both falling off in this way, side by side: when they got up again, they shook hands, and then the Red Knight mounted and galloped off.

"It was a glorious victory, wasn't it?" said the White Knight, as he came up panting.

"I don't know," Alice said doubtfully. "I don't want to be anybody's prisoner. I want to be a Queen."

"So you will, when you've crossed the next brook," said the White Knight. "I'll see you safe to the end of the wood — and then I must go back, you know. That's the end of my move."

"Thank you very much," said Alice. "May I help you off with your helmet?" It was evidently more than he could manage by himself; however, she managed to shake him out of it at last.

"Now one can breathe more easily," said the Knight, putting back his shaggy hair with both hands, and turning his gentle face and large mild eyes to Alice. She thought she had never seen such a strange-looking soldier in all her life.

He was dressed in tin armor, which seemed to fit him very badly, and he had a queer-shaped little deal box fastened across his shoulders, upside down, and with the lid hanging open. Alice looked at it with great curiosity.

"I see you're admiring my little box," the Knight said in a friendly tone. "It's my own invention — to keep clothes and sandwiches in. You see, I carry it upside-down, so that the rain can't get in."

"But the things can get *out*," Alice gently remarked. "Do you know the lid's open?"

"I didn't know it," the Knight said, a shade of vexation passing over his face. "Then all the things must have fallen out! And the box is no use without them." He unfastened it as he spoke, and was just going to throw it into the bushes, when a sudden thought seemed to strike him, and he hung it carefully on a tree. "Can you guess why I did that?" he said to Alice.

Alice shook her head.

"In hopes some bees may make a nest in it — then I should get the honey."

"But you've got a bee-hive — or something like one — fastened to the saddle," said Alice.

"Yes, it's a very good bee-hive," the Knight said, in a discontented tone, "one of the best kind. But

not a single bee has come near it yet. And the other
thing is a mouse-trap. I suppose the mice keep the
bees out — or the bees keep the mice out, I don't
know which."

"I was wondering what the mouse-trap was for,"
said Alice. "It isn't very likely there would be any
mice on the horse's back."

"Not very likely, perhaps," said the Knight; "but
if they *do* come, I don't choose to have them running
all about."

"You see," he went on after a pause, "it's as well to
be provided for *everything*. That's the reason the horse
has all those anklets round his feet."

"But what are they for?" Alice asked in a tone of
great curiosity.

"To guard against the bites of sharks," the Knight
replied. "It's an invention of my own. And now help
me on. I'll go with you to the end of the wood.
What's that dish for?"

"It's meant for plum-cake," said Alice.

"We'd better take it with us," the Knight said.
"It'll come in handy if we can find any plum-cake.
Help me to get it into this bag."

This took a long time to manage, though Alice held
the bag open very carefully, because the Knight was so
very awkward in putting in the dish: the first two or
three times that he tried he fell in himself instead.
"It's rather a tight fit, you see," he said, as they got it
in at last; "there are so many candlesticks in the bag."
And he hung it to the saddle, which was already loaded
with bunches of carrots, and fire-irons, and many other
things.

"I hope you've got your hair well fastened on?" he continued, as they set off.

"Only in the usual way," Alice said, smiling.

"That's hardly enough," he said anxiously. "You see the wind is so *very* strong here. It's as strong as soup."

"Have you invented a plan for keeping the hair from being blown off?" Alice inquired.

"Not yet," said the Knight. "But I've got a plan for keeping it from *falling* off."

"I should like to hear it, very much."

"First you take an upright stick," said the Knight. "Then you make your hair creep up it, like a fruit-tree. Now the reason hair falls off is because it hangs *down* —things never fall *upward*, you know. It's a plan of my own invention. You may try it if you like."

It didn't sound a comfortable plan, Alice thought, and for a few minutes she walked on in silence, puzzling over the idea, and every now and then stopping to help the poor Knight, who certainly was *not* a good rider.

Whenever the horse stopped (which it did very often), he fell off in front; and whenever it went on again (which it generally did rather suddenly), he fell off behind. Otherwise he kept on pretty well, except that he had a habit of now and then falling off sideways; and as he generally did this on the side on which Alice was walking, she soon found that it was the best plan not to walk *quite* close to the horse.

" I'm afraid you've not had much practice in riding," she ventured to say, as she was helping him up from his fifth tumble.

The Knight looked very much surprised, and a little offended at the remark. " What makes you say that ? " he asked, as he scrambled back into the saddle, keeping hold of Alice's hair with one hand, to save himself from falling over on the other side.

" Because people don't fall off quite so often, when they've had much practice."

" I've had plenty of practice," the Knight said very gravely; " plenty of practice ! "

Alice could think of nothing better to say than " Indeed ? " but she said it as heartily as she could. They went on a little way in silence after this, the Knight with his eyes shut, muttering to himself, and Alice watching anxiously for the next tumble.

" The great art of riding," the Knight suddenly began in a loud voice, waving his right arm as he spoke, " is to keep —— " Here the sentence ended as suddenly as it had begun, as the Knight fell heavily on the top of his head exactly in the path where Alice was walking. She was quite frightened this time, and said in an anxious tone, as she picked him up, " I hope no bones are broken ? "

" None to speak of," the Knight said, as if he didn't mind breaking two or three of them. " The great art

of riding, as I was saying is — to keep your balance
properly. Like this, you know —— "

He let go the bridle, and stretched out both his arms
to show Alice what he meant, and this time he fell flat
on his back, right under the horse's feet.

" Plenty of practice ! " he went on repeating, all the
time that Alice was getting him on his feet again.
" Plenty of practice ! "

" It's too ridiculous ! " cried Alice, losing all her
patience this time. " You ought to have a wooden
horse on wheels, that you ought ! "

" Does that kind go smoothly ? " the Knight asked,
in a tone of great interest, clasping his arms round the
horse's neck as he spoke, just in time to save himself
from tumbling off again.

" Much more smoothly than a live horse," Alice said,
with a little scream of laughter, in spite of all she
could do to prevent it.

" I'll get one," the Knight said thoughtfully to himself. " One or two — several."

There was a short silence after this, and then the
Knight went on again. " I'm a great hand at inventing things. Now, I daresay you noticed, the last
time you picked me up, that I was looking rather
thoughtful ? "

" You *were* a little grave," said Alice.

" Well just then I was inventing a new way of
getting over a gate — would you like to hear it ? "

" Very much indeed," Alice said politely.

" I'll tell you how I came to think of it," said the
Knight. " You see, I said to myself, ' The only difficulty is with the feet; the *head* is high enough already.'

Now, first I put my head on the top of the gate — then the head's high enough — then I stand on my head — then the feet are high enough, you see — then I'm over, you see."

"Yes, I suppose you'd be over when that was done," Alice said thoughtfully; "but don't you think it would be rather hard?"

"I haven't tried it yet," the Knight said, gravely, "so I can't tell for certain — but I'm afraid it *would* be a little hard."

He looked so vexed at the idea, that Alice changed the subject hastily. "What a curious helmet you've got!" she said cheerfully. "Is that your invention too?"

The Knight looked down proudly at his helmet, which hung from the saddle. "Yes," he said, "but I've invented a better one than that — like a sugar loaf. When I used to wear it, if I fell off the horse it always touched the ground directly. So I had a *very* little way to fall, you see. But there *was* the danger of falling *into* it, to be sure. That happened to me once — and the worst of it was, before I could get out again, the other White Knight came and put it on. He thought it was his own helmet."

The Knight looked so solemn about it that Alice did not dare to laugh. "I'm afraid you must have hurt him," she said in a trembling voice, "being on the top of his head."

"I had to kick him, of course," the Knight said, very seriously. "And then he took the helmet off again — but it took hours and hours to get me out. I was as fast as — as lightning, you know."

"But that's a different kind of fastness," Alice objected.

The Knight shook his head. "It was all kinds of fastness with me, I can assure you!" he said. He raised his hands in some excitement as he said this, and instantly rolled out of the saddle and fell headlong into a deep ditch.

Alice ran to the side of the ditch to look for him. She was rather startled by the fall, as for some time he had kept on very well, and she was afraid that he really *was* hurt this time. However, though she could see nothing but the soles of his feet, she was much relieved to hear that he was talking on in his usual tone.

"All kinds of fastness," he repeated: "but it was careless of him to put another man's helmet on — with the man in it, too."

"How *can* you go on talking so quietly, head downward?" Alice asked, as she dragged him out by the feet and laid him in a heap on the bank.

The Knight looked surprised at the question. "What does it matter where my body happens to be?" he said. "My mind goes on working all the same. In fact, the more head downward I am, the more I keep inventing new things. Now the cleverest thing of the sort that I ever did," he went on after a pause, "was inventing a new pudding during the meat-course."

"In time to have it cooked for the next course?" said Alice. "Well, that *was* quick work, certainly!"

"Well, not the *next* course," the Knight said in a slow, thoughtful tone: "no, certainly not the next *course.*"

"Then it would have to be the next day. I suppose you wouldn't have two pudding-courses in one dinner?"

"Well, not the *next* day," the Knight repeated as before: "not the next *day.* In fact, he went on, holding his head down, and his voice getting lower and lower, "I don't believe that pudding ever *was* cooked! In fact, I don't believe that pudding ever *will* be cooked! And yet it was a very clever pudding to invent."

"What did you mean it to be made of?" Alice asked, hoping to cheer him up, for the poor Knight seemed quite low-spirited about it.

"It began with blotting-paper," the Knight answered with a groan.

"That wouldn't be very nice, I'm afraid——"

"Not very nice *alone*," he interrupted, quite eagerly: "but you've no idea what a difference it makes, mixing it with other things — such as gunpowder and sealing-wax. And here I must leave you." They had just come to the end of the wood.

Alice could only look puzzled: she was thinking of the pudding.

"You are sad," the Knight said, in an anxious tone: "let me sing a song to comfort you."

"Is it very long?" Alice asked, for she had heard a good deal of poetry that day.

"It's long," said the Knight, "but it's very, *very*

beautiful. Everybody that hears me sing it—either it brings the *tears* into their eyes, or else——"

"Or else what?" said Alice, for the Knight had made a sudden pause.

"Or else it doesn't, you know. The name of the song is called '*Haddock's Eyes.*'"

"Oh, that's the name of the song, is it?" Alice said, trying to feel interested.

"No, you don't understand," the Knight said, looking a little vexed. "That's what the name is *called*. The name really is '*The Aged Aged Man.*'"

"Then I ought to have said 'That's what the *song* is called?'" Alice corrected herself.

"No, you oughtn't: that's quite another thing! The *song* is called '*Ways and Means:*' but that's only what it's *called*, you know!"

"Well, what *is* the song, then?" said Alice, who was by this time completely bewildered.

"I was coming to that," the Knight said. "The song really is '*A-Sitting on a Gate:*' and the tune's my own invention."

So saying, he stopped his horse and let the reins fall on its neck: then, slowly beating time with one hand, and with a faint smile lighting up his gentle foolish face as if he enjoyed the music of his song, he began.

Of all the strange things that Alice saw in her journey "Through the Looking-Glass," this was the one that she always remembered most clearly. Years afterward she could bring the whole scene back again, as if it had been only yesterday—the mild blue eyes and kindly smile of the Knight—the setting sun gleaming through his hair, and shining on his armor in a blaze of light that quite dazzled her — the horse quietly moving about, with the reins hanging loose on his neck, cropping the grass at her feet — and the black shadows of the forest behind — all this she took in like a picture, as, with one hand shading her eyes, she leaned against a tree, watching the strange pair, and listening, in a half dream, to the melancholy music of the song.

"But the tune *isn't* his own invention," she said to herself : "it's '*I give thee all, I can no more.*'" She stood and listened very attentively, but no tears came into her eyes.

> "I'll tell thee everything I can ;
> There's little to relate.
> I saw an aged aged man,
> A-sitting on a gate.
> 'Who are you, aged man?' I said.
> 'And how is it you live?'
> And his answer trickled through my head
> Like water through a sieve.
>
> He said, 'I look for butterflies
> That sleep among the wheat :
> I make them into mutton-pies,
> And sell them in the street.
> I sell them unto men,' he said,
> 'Who sail on stormy seas ;
> And that's the way I get my bread —
> A trifle, if you please.'
>
> But I was thinking of a plan
> To dye one's whiskers green,
> And always use so large a fan
> That they could not be seen.

So, having no reply to give
  To what the old man said,
I cried, ' Come, tell me how you live!'
  And thumped him on the head.

His accents mild took up the tale:
  He said, 'I go my ways,
And when I find a mountain-rill
  I set it in a blaze;
And thence they make a stuff they call
  Rowlands' Macassar Oil —
Yet twopence-halfpenny is all
  They give me for my toil.'

But I was thinking of a way
  To feed oneself on batter,
And so go on from day to day
  Getting a little fatter.
  I shook him well from side
    to side,
Until his face was blue:
  ' Come, tell me how you
    live,' I cried,
  'And what it is you do!'

He said, 'I hunt for had-
    docks' eyes
Among the heather bright,
And work them into waistcoat-buttons
  In the silent night.
And these I do not sell for gold
  Or coin of silvery shine,
But for a copper halfpenny,
  And that will purchase nine.

'I sometimes dig for buttered rolls,
  Or set limed twigs for crabs:

I sometimes search the grassy knolls
  For wheels of Hansom-cabs.
And that's the way' (he gave a wink)
  'By which I get my wealth —
And very gladly will I drink
  Your Honor's noble health.'

I heard him then, for I had just
  Completed my design
To keep the Menai bridge from rust
  By boiling it in wine.
I thanked him much for telling me
  The way he got his wealth,
But chiefly for his wish that he
  Might drink my noble health.

And now, if e'er by chance I put
  My fingers into glue,
Or madly squeeze a right-hand foot
  Into a left-hand shoe,
Or if I drop upon my toe
  A very heavy weight
I weep, for it reminds me so
Of that old man I used to know —
Whose look was mild, whose speech was slow,
Whose hair was whiter than the snow,
Whose face was very like a crow,
With eyes like cinders, all aglow,
Who seemed distracted with his woe,
Who rocked his body to and fro,
And muttered mumblingly and low,
As if his mouth were full of dough,
Who snorted like a buffalo —
That summer evening, long ago,
  A-sitting on a gate."

As the Knight sang the last words of the ballad, he
gathered up the reins, and turned his horse's head along

the road by which they had come. "You've only a few yards to go," he said, "down the hill and over that little brook, and then you'll be a Queen. But you'll stay and see me off first?" he added, as Alice turned with an eager look in the direction to which he pointed. "I sha'n't be long. You'll wait and wave your handkerchief when I get to that turn in the road? I think it'll encourage me, you see."

"Of course I'll wait," said Alice: "and thank you very much for coming so far — and for the song — I liked it very much."

"I hope so," the Knight said doubtfully: "but you didn't cry so much as I thought you would."

So they shook hands, and then the Knight rode slowly away into the forest. "It won't take long to see him *off*, I expect," Alice said to herself, as she stood watching him. "There he goes! Right on his head as usual! However, he gets on again pretty easily — that comes of having so many things hung round the horse." So she went on talking to herself as she watched the horse walking leisurely along the road, and the Knight tumbling off, first on one side and then on the other. After the fourth or fifth tumble he reached the turn, and then she waved her handkerchief to him, and waited till he was out of sight.

"I hope it encouraged him," she said, as she turned to run down the hill: "and now for the last brook, and to be a Queen! How grand it sounds!" A very few steps brought her to the edge of the brook. "The Eighth Square at last!" she cried, as she bounded across, and threw herself down to rest on a lawn as soft as moss, with little flower-beds dotted about it here and there. "Oh, how glad I am to get here! And what *is* this on my head?" she exclaimed in a tone of dismay, as she put her hands up to something very heavy, that fitted tight all round her head.

"But how *can* it have got there without my knowing it?" she said to herself, as she lifted it off, and set it on her lap to make out what it could possibly be.

It was a golden crown.

THE PICKWICKIANS DISPORT THEM-SELVES ON THE ICE

By CHARLES DICKENS.

MR. PICKWICK.

WELL, Sam," said Mr. Pickwick as that favored servitor entered his bedchamber with his warm water, on the morning of Christmas Day, "Still frosty?"

"Water in the wash-hand basin's a mask o' ice, sir," responded Sam.

"Severe weather, Sam," observed Mr. Pickwick.

"Fine time for them as is well wropped up, as the Polar Bear said to himself, ven he was practising his skating," replied Mr. Weller.

"I shall be down in a quarter of an hour, Sam," said Mr. Pickwick, untying his nightcap.

"Wery good, sir," replied Sam. "There's a couple o' Sawbones downstairs."

"A couple of what!" exclaimed Mr. Pickwick, sitting up in bed.

"A couple o' Sawbones," said Sam.

"What's a Sawbones?" inquired Mr. Pickwick, not

181

quite certain whether it was a live animal, or something to eat.

"What! don't you know what a Sawbones is, sir?" inquired Mr. Weller; "I thought everybody know'd as a Sawbones was a Surgeon."

"Oh, a Surgeon, eh?" said Mr. Pickwick with a smile.

"Just that, sir," replied Sam. "These here ones as is below, though, ain't reg'lar thoroughbred Sawbones; they're only in trainin'."

SAM WELLER.

"In other words they're medical students, I suppose?" said Mr. Pickwick.

Sam Weller nodded assent.

"I am glad of it," said Mr. Pickwick, casting his nightcap energetically on the counterpane. "They are fine fellows; very fine fellows; with judgments matured by observation and reflection; and tastes refined by reading and study. I am very glad of it."

"They're a smokin' cigars by the kitchen fire," said Sam.

"Ah!" observed Mr. Pickwick, rubbing his hands, "overflowing with kindly feelings and animal spirits. Just what I like to see!"

"And one on 'em," said Sam, not noticing his master's interruption, "one on 'em's got his legs on the table, and is a drinkin' brandy neat, vile the t'other one — him in the barnacles — has got a barrel o' oysters atween his knees, wich he's openin' like steam, and as fast as he eats 'em, he takes a aim vith the shells at young dropsy, who's a sittin' down fast asleep in the chimbley corner."

"Eccentricities of genius, Sam," said Mr. Pickwick. "You may retire."

Sam did retire accordingly; Mr. Pickwick, at the expiration of the quarter of an hour, went down to breakfast.

"Here he is at last," said old Wardle. "Pickwick, this is Miss Allen's brother, Mr. Benjamin Allen — Ben we call him, and so may you if you like. This gentleman is his very particular friend, Mr. —— "

"Mr. Bob Sawyer," interposed Mr. Benjamin Allen; whereupon Mr. Bob Sawyer and Mr. Benjamin Allen laughed in concert.

Mr. Pickwick bowed to Bob Sawyer, and Bob Sawyer bowed to Mr. Pickwick; Bob and his very particular friend then applied themselves most assiduously to the eatables before them; and Mr. Pickwick had an opportunity of glancing at them both.

Mr. Benjamin Allen was a coarse, stout, thick-set young man, with black hair cut rather short, and a white face cut rather long. He was embellished with spectacles, and wore a white neckerchief. Below his single-breasted black surtout, which was buttoned up to his chin, appeared the usual number of pepper-and-salt colored legs, terminating in a pair of imperfectly polished boots. Although his coat was short in the sleeves, it disclosed no vestige of a linen wristband; and although there was quite enough of his face to admit of the encroachment of a shirt-collar, it was not graced by the smallest approach to that appendage. He presented, altogether, rather a mildewy appearance: and emitted a fragrant odor of full-flavored Cubas.

Mr. Bob Sawyer, who was habited in a coarse blue coat, which, without being either a great-coat or a surtout, partook of the nature and qualities of both, had about him that sort of slovenly smartness, and swaggering gait, which is peculiar to young gentlemen who smoke in the streets by day, shout and scream in the same by night, call waiters by their Christian names, and do various other acts and deeds of an equally facetious description. He wore a pair of plaid trousers, and a large rough double-breasted-waistcoat; and out of doors, carried a thick stick with a big top. He eschewed gloves: and looked, upon the whole, something like a dissipated Robinson Crusoe.

Such were the two worthies to whom Mr. Pickwick was introduced, as he took his seat at the breakfast table on Christmas morning.

"Splendid morning, gentlemen," said Mr. Pickwick.

Mr. Bob Sawyer slightly nodded his assent to the proposition, and asked Mr. Benjamin Allen for the mustard.

"Have you come far this morning, gentlemen?" inquired Mr. Pickwick.

"Blue Lion at Muggleton," briefly responded Mr Allen.

"You should have joined us last night," said Mr. Pickwick.

"So we should," replied Bob Sawyer, "but the brandy was too good to leave in a hurry: wasn't it, Ben?"

"Certainly," said Mr. Benjamin Allen; "and the cigars were not bad, or the pork chops either; were they, Bob?"

"Decidedly not," said Bob. The particular friends resumed their attack upon the breakfast, more freely than before, as if the recollection of last night's supper had imparted a new relish to the meal.

"Peg away, Bob," said Mr. Allen to his companion, encouragingly.

"So I do," replied Bob Sawyer. And so, to do him justice, he did.

"Nothing like dissecting, to give one an appetite," said Mr. Bob Sawyer, looking round the table. . . .

"Hush, hush, gentlemen, pray," said Mr. Pickwick, "I hear the ladies."

As Mr. Pickwick spoke, the ladies, gallantly escorted by Messrs. Snodgrass, Winkle, and Tupman, returned from an early walk.

"Why, Ben!" said Arabella, in a tone which expressed more surprise than pleasure at the sight of her brother.

"Come to take you home to-morrow," replied Benjamin.

Mr. Winkle turned pale.

"Don't you see Bob Sawyer, Arabella?" inquired Mr. Benjamin Allen, somewhat reproachfully. Arabella gracefully held out her hand, in acknowledgment of Bob Sawyer's presence. A thrill of hatred struck to Mr. Winkle's heart, as Bob Sawyer inflicted on the proffered hand a perceptible squeeze.

"Ben dear!" said Arabella, blushing, "have — have — you been introduced to Mr. Winkle?"

"I have not been, but I shall be very happy to be, Arabella," replied her brother gravely. Here Mr. Allen bowed grimly to Mr. Winkle, while Mr. Winkle and Mr. Bob Sawyer glanced mutual distrust out of the corners of their eyes.

The arrival of the two new visitors, and the consequent check upon Mr. Winkle and the young lady with the fur round her boots, would in all probability have proved a very unpleasant interruption to the hilarity of the party, had not the cheerfulness of Mr. Pickwick, and the good humor of the host, been exerted to the very utmost for the common weal. Mr. Winkle gradually insinuated himself into the good graces of Mr. Benjamin Allen, and even joined in a friendly conversation with Mr. Bob Sawyer; who, enlivened with the brandy, and the breakfast, and the talking, gradually ripened into a state of extreme facetiousness, and related with much glee an agreeable anecdote, about the removal of a tumor on some gentleman's head; which he illustrated by means of an oyster knife and a half-quartern loaf, to the great edification of the assembled company. Then, the whole train went to church, where Mr. Benjamin Allen fell fast asleep: while Mr. Bob Sawyer abstracted his thoughts from worldly matters by the ingenious process of carving his name on the seat of the pew, in corpulent letters of four inches long.

"Now," said Wardle, after a substantial lunch, with

the agreeable items of strong beer and cherry-brandy, had been done ample justice to; "what say you to an hour on the ice? We shall have plenty of time."

"Capital!" said Mr. Benjamin Allen.

"Prime!" ejaculated Mr. Bob Sawyer.

"You skate of course, Winkle?" said Wardle.

"Ye — yes; oh, yes;" replied Mr. Winkle. "I — I — am *rather* out of practice."

"Oh, *do* skate, Mr. Winkle," said Arabella. "I like to see it so much."

"Oh, it is *so* graceful," said another young lady.

A third young lady said it was elegant, and a fourth expressed her opinion that it was "swan-like."

"I should be very happy, I'm sure," said Mr. Winkle, reddening, "but I have no skates."

This objection was at once overruled. Trundle had a couple of pair, and the fat boy announced that there were half a dozen more down-stairs: whereat Mr. Winkle expressed exquisite delight, and looked exquisitely uncomfortable.

Old Wardle led the way to a pretty large sheet of ice; and the fat boy and Mr. Weller, having shovelled and swept away the snow which had fallen on it during the night, Mr. Bob Sawyer adjusted his skates with a dexterity which to Mr. Winkle was perfectly marvellous and described circles with his left leg, and cut figures of eight; and inscribed upon the ice, without once stopping for breath, a great many other pleasant and astonishing devices, to the excessive satisfaction of Mr. Pickwick, Mr. Tupman, and the ladies: which reached a pitch of positive enthusiasm when old Wardle and Benjamin Allen, assisted by the aforesaid Bob

Sawyer, performed some mystic evolutions which they called a reel.

All this time, Mr. Winkle, with his face and hands blue with the cold, had been forcing a gimlet into the soles of his feet, and putting his skates on, with the points behind, and getting the straps into a very complicated and entangled state, with the assistance of Mr. Snodgrass, who knew rather less about skates than a Hindoo.   At length, however, with the assistance of Mr. Weller, the unfortunate skates were firmly screwed and buckled on, and Mr. Winkle was raised to his feet.

" Now, then, sir," said Sam in an encouraging tone; " off vith you, and show 'em how to do it."

" Stop, Sam, stop ! " said Mr. Winkle, trembling violently, and clutching hold of Sam's arms with the grasp of a drowning man.   " How slippery it is, Sam ! "

" Not an uncommon thing upon ice, sir," replied Mr. Weller.   " Hold up, sir ! "

This last observation of Mr. Weller's bore reference to a demonstration Mr. Winkle made at the instant, of a frantic desire to throw his feet in the air, and dash the back of his head on the ice.

" These — these — are very awkward skates; ain't they, Sam ? " inquired Mr. Winkle, staggering.

" I'm afeerd there's an orkard gen'lm'n in 'em, sir," replied Sam.

" Now, Winkle," cried Mr. Pickwick, quite unconscious that there was anything the matter.   " Come; the ladies are all anxiety."

" Yes, yes," replied Mr. Winkle, with a ghastly smile.   " I'm coming."

"Just a goin' to begin," said Sam, endeavoring to disengage himself. "Now, sir, start off!"

"Stop an instant, Sam," gasped Mr. Winkle, clinging most affectionately to Mr. Weller. "I find I've got a couple of coats at home, that I don't want, Sam. You may have them, Sam."

"Thank'ee, sir," replied Mr. Weller.

"Never mind touching your hat, Sam," said Mr. Winkle, hastily. "You needn't take your hand away to do that. I meant to have given you five shillings this morning for a Christmas-box, Sam. I'll give it you this afternoon, Sam."

"You're wery good sir," replied Mr. Weller.

"Just hold me at first, Sam; will you?" said Mr. Winkle. "There — that's right. I shall soon get in the way of it, Sam. Not too fast, Sam; not too fast."

Mr. Winkle stooping forward with his body half doubled up, was being assisted over the ice by Mr. Weller, in a very singular and un-swan-like manner, when Mr. Pickwick most innocently shouted from the opposite bank, —

"Sam!"

"Sir?" said Mr. Weller.

"Here. I want you."

"Let go, sir," said Sam. "Don't you hear the governor a callin'? Let go, sir."

With a violent effort, Mr. Weller disengaged himself from the grasp of the agonized Pickwickian; and, in so doing, administered a considerable impetus to the unhappy Mr. Winkle. With an accuracy which no degree of dexterity or practice could have insured, that unfortunate gentleman bore swiftly down into the centre of the reel, at the very moment when Mr. Bob Sawyer was performing a flourish of unparalleled beauty. Mr. Winkle struck wildly against him, and with a loud crash they both fell heavily down. Mr. Pickwick ran to the spot. Bob Sawyer had risen to his feet, but Mr. Winkle was far too wise to do anything of the kind, on skates. He was seated on the ice, making spasmodic efforts to smile ; but anguish was depicted on every lineament of his countenance.

"Are you hurt ? " inquired Mr. Benjamin Allen, with great anxiety.

" Not much," said Mr. Winkle, rubbing his back very hard.

" I wish you'd let me bleed you,"

"HE WAS SEATED ON THE ICE." said Mr. Benjamin, with great eagerness.

" No, thank you," replied Mr. Winkle hurriedly.

" I really think you had better," said Allen.

" Thank you," replied Mr. Winkle; " I'd **rather** not."

" What do you think, Mr. Pickwick ? " inquired Bob Sawyer.

Mr. Pickwick was excited and indignant. He beckoned to Mr. Weller, and said in a stern voice, " Take his skates off."

"No; but really I had scarcely begun," remonstrated Mr. Winkle.

"Take his skates off," repeated Mr. Pickwick firmly.

The command was not to be resisted. Mr. Winkle allowed Sam to obey it, in silence.

"Lift him up," said Mr. Pickwick. Sam assisted him to rise.

Mr. Pickwick retired a few paces apart from the by-standers; and, beckoning his friend to approach, fixed a searching look upon him, and uttered in a low, but distinct and emphatic tone, these remarkable words, —

"You're a humbug, sir."

"A what!" said Mr. Winkle, starting.

"A humbug, sir. I will speak plainer, if you wish it. An impostor, sir."

With these words, Mr. Pickwick turned slowly on his heel, and joined his friends.

While Mr. Pickwick was delivering himself of the sentiment just recorded, Mr. Weller and the fat boy, having by their joint endeavors cut out a slide, were exercising themselves thereupon, in a very masterly and brilliant manner. Sam Weller, in particular, was displaying that beautiful feat of fancy sliding, which is currently denominated "knocking at the cobbler's door," and which was achieved by skimming over the ice on one foot, and occasionally giving a twopenny postman's knock upon it, with the other. It was a good long slide, and there was something in the motion which Mr. Pickwick, who was very cold with standing still, could not help envying.

"It looks a nice warm exercise, that, doesn't it?" he inquired of Wardle, when that gentleman was

thoroughly out of breath, by reason of the indefati-
gable manner in which he had converted his legs into
a pair of compasses, and drawn complicated problems
on the ice.

"Ah, it does, indeed," replied Wardle. "Do you
slide?"

"I used to do so, on the gutters, when I was a boy,"
replied Mr. Pickwick.

"Try it now," said Wardle.

"Oh do, please, Mr. Pickwick," cried all the ladies.

"I should be very happy to afford you any amusement," replied Mr. Pickwick, "but I haven't done
such a thing these thirty years."

"Pooh! pooh! nonsense!" said Wardle, dragging off
his skates with the impetuosity which characterized all
his proceedings. "Here; I'll keep you company; come
along." And away went the good-tempered old fellow
down the slide, with a rapidity which came very close
upon Mr. Weller, and beat the fat boy all to nothing.

Mr. Pickwick paused, considered, pulled off his gloves
and put them in his hat: took two or three short runs:
balked himself as often; and at last took another run,
and went slowly and gravely down the slide, with his
feet about a yard and a quarter apart, amidst the gratified shouts of all the spectators.

"Keep the pot a bilin', sir!" said Sam; and down
went Wardle again, and then Mr. Pickwick, and then
Sam, and then Mr. Winkle, and then Mr. Bob Sawyer,
and then the fat boy, and then Mr. Snodgrass, following closely upon each other's heels, and running after
each other with as much eagerness as if all their future
prospects in life depended on their expedition.

It was the most intensely interesting thing, to observe the manner in which Mr. Pickwick performed his share in the ceremony: to watch the torture of anxiety with which he viewed the person behind, gaining upon him at the immi-

nent hazard of tripping him up: to see him gradually expend the painful force which he had put on at first, and turn slowly round on the slide, with his face towards the point from which he started: to contemplate the playful smile which mantled on his face when he had accomplished the distance, and the eagerness with which he turned round when he had done so, and ran after his predecessor: his black

MR. PICKWICK PERFORMED HIS
SHARE IN THE CEREMONY.

gaiters tripping pleasantly through the snow, and his eyes beaming cheerfulness and gladness through his spectacles. And when he was knocked down (which happened upon the average every third round), it was the most invigorating sight that can possibly be imagined, to behold him gather up his hat, gloves, and handkerchief, with a glowing countenance, and resume his station in the rank, with an ardor and enthusiasm that nothing could abate.

The sport was at its height, the sliding was at the quickest, the laughter was at the loudest, when a sharp, smart crack was heard. There was a quick rush towards the bank, a wild scream from the ladies, and a shout from Mr. Tupman. A large mass of ice disappeared; the water bubbled up over it; Mr. Pickwick's hat, gloves, and handkerchief were floating on the surface; and this was all of Mr. Pickwick that anybody could see.

Dismay and anguish were depicted on every countenance; the males turned pale, and the females fainted; Mr. Snodgrass and Mr. Winkle grasped each other by the hand, and gazed at the spot where their leader had gone down, with frenzied eagerness; while Mr. Tupman, by way of rendering the promptest assistance, and at the same time conveying to any persons who might be within hearing, the clearest possible notion of the catastrophe, ran off across the country at his utmost speed, screaming "Fire!" with all his might.

It was at this very moment, when old Wardle and Sam Weller were approaching the hole with cautious steps, and Mr. Benjamin Allen was holding a hurried consultation with Mr. Bob Sawyer on the advisability of bleeding the company generally, as an improving little bit of professional practice—it was at this very moment that a face, head, and shoulders emerged from beneath the water, and disclosed the features and spectacles of Mr. Pickwick.

"Keep yourself up for an instant — for only one in-stant," bawled Mr. Snodgrass.

"Yes, do; let me implore you — for my sake," roared Mr. Winkle, deeply affected. The adjuration was rather unnecessary; the probability being, that if Mr. Pickwick had declined to keep himself up for any-body else's sake, it would have occurred to him that he might as well do so for his own.

"Do you feel the bottom there, old fellow?" said Wardle.

"Yes, certainly," replied Mr. Pickwick, wringing the water from his head and face, and gasping for breath. "I fell upon my back. I couldn't get on my feet at first."

The clay upon so much of Mr. Pickwick's coat as was yet visible, bore testimony to the accuracy of this statement; and as the fears of the spectators were still further relieved by the fat boy's suddenly recol-lecting that the water was nowhere more than five feet deep, prodigies of valor were performed to get him out. After a vast quantity of splashing, and cracking, and struggling, Mr. Pickwick was at length fairly extri-cated from his unpleasant position, and once more stood on dry land.

"Oh, he'll catch his death of cold," said Emily.

"Dear old thing!" said Arabella. "Let me wrap this shawl round you, Mr. Pickwick."

"Ah, that's the best thing you can do," said Wardle; "and when you've got it on, run home as fast as your legs can carry you, and jump into bed directly."

A dozen shawls were offered on the instant. Three or four of the thickest having been selected, Mr. Pickwick was wrapped up, and started off, under the guidance of Mr. Weller; presenting the singular phenomenon of an elderly gentleman, dripping wet, and without a hat, with his arms bound down to his sides, skimming over the ground, without any clearly defined purpose, at the rate of six good English miles an hour.

But Mr. Pickwick cared not for appearances in such an extreme case, and urged on by Sam Weller, he kept up at the very top of his speed until he reached the door of Manor Farm, where Mr. Tupman had arrived some five minutes before, and had frightened the old lady into palpitations of the heart, by impressing her with the unalterable conviction that the kitchen chimney was on fire — a calamity which always presented itself in glowing colors to the old lady's mind, when anybody about her evinced the smallest agitation.

"AN ELDERLY GENTLEMAN, . . . SKIMMING OVER THE GROUND."

BARON MUNCHAUSEN IN RUSSIA

By R. E. RASPÉ.

The name of Munchausen has come to stand for the type of the narrator who boldly exaggerates his exploits beyond the limits of credibility. Karl Friedrich Hieronymus Baron von Münchausen, belonging to an ancient Hanoverian family which is still in existence, was born in 1720, and after serving in Russian campaigns against the Turks, died in 1797. The collection of marvellous stories attributed to him was largely written by a talented and rascally Hanoverian named Rudolf Erich Raspé. It was first published in English in 1785. Many of the marvellous stories were based on mediæval German jokes.

I SET off on a journey to Russia, in the midst of winter, from a just notion that frost and snow must, of course, mend the roads, which every traveller had described as uncommonly bad through the northern parts of Germany, Poland, Courland, and Livonia. I went on horseback, as it is the most convenient manner of travelling, provided, however, that rider and horse are in good condition. In this way there is not the likelihood of your having an affair of honor on account of a groundless quarrel with any worthy host, nor being compelled to stop before every inn, at the mercy of the postillion swindling you. I was but lightly clothed, and of this I felt the inconvenience the more I advanced north-east. What must not a poor old man have suffered in that severe weather and climate, whom I saw on a bleak common in Poland, lying on the road, helpless, shivering, and hardly having wherewithal to cover his nakedness! I pitied the poor soul. Though I felt the severity of the air myself, I threw my mantle over him, and immediately I heard a voice from the heavens, blessing me for that piece of charity, saying —

"You will be rewarded, my son, for this in time."

I went on; night and darkness overtook me. No sight or sound of a village was to be met with. The country was covered with snow, and I was unacquainted with the road.

Tired, I alighted, and fastened my horse to something like the pointed stump of a tree, which appeared above the snow; for the sake of safety, I placed my pistols under my arm, and lay down on the snow, where I slept so soundly that I did not open my eyes till full daylight. It is not easy to conceive my astonishment, to find myself in the midst of a village, lying in a churchyard; nor was my horse to be seen, but I heard him soon after, neigh somewhere above me. On looking upwards, I beheld him hanging by his bridle to the weather-cock of the steeple. Matters were now very plain to me; the village had been covered with snow overnight; a sudden change of weather had taken place; I had sunk down to the churchyard whilst asleep, gently, and in the same

proportion as the snow had melted away; and what
in the dark I had taken to be a stump of a little tree
appearing above the snow, to which I had tied my
horse, proved to have been the cross or weather-cock
of the steeple!

Without long consideration, I took one of my pistols,
shot the bridle in two, brought down the horse, and
proceeded on my journey. [Here the Baron seems to
have forgot his feelings; he should certainly have
ordered his horse a feed of corn, after fasting so long.]

.   .   .   .

You may easily imagine that I spent much of my
time out of town, with such gallant fellows as knew
how to make the most of an open forest country.
The very recollection of those amusements gives
me fresh spirits, and creates a warm wish for a
repetition of them. One morning I saw through
the windows of my bedroom that a large pond,
not far off, was covered with wild ducks. In an
instant I took my gun from the corner, ran down-
stairs, and out of the house in such a hurry, that
I imprudently struck my face against the door-post.
Fire flew out of my eyes, but it did not prevent my
intention; I soon came within shot, when, levelling
my piece, I observed, to my sorrow, that even the flint
had sprung from the cock, by the violence of the shock
I had just received. There was no time to be lost. I
presently remembered the effect it had on my eyes,
therefore opened the pan, levelled my piece against the
wild fowls, and my fist against one of my eyes. [The
Baron's eyes have retained fire ever since, and appear
particularly illuminated when he relates this anecdote.]

A hearty blow drew sparks again; the shot went off, and I killed fifty brace of ducks, twenty widgeons, and three couple of teals.

Presence of mind is the soul of manly exercises. If soldiers and sailors owe to it many of their lucky escapes, hunters and sportsmen are not less beholden to it for many of their successes. Thus, for example, I remember one day I saw on the lake, to the shore of which one of my wanderings had brought me, some dozens of wild ducks, too scattered, however, for me to hope that I alone with my gun could reach any number of them. As a climax of misfortune, I had my last charge in my gun. I remembered, however, that I had in my game-bag a piece of fat, the remains of the provisions of which I had a supply when starting. I fastened a morsel of the fat to my bag-string, which I cut in two, and the four threads of which I joined end to end. Afterwards I lay amongst the rushes on the bank. I threw my bait, and soon I had the satisfaction to see the first duck approach it eagerly and swallow it. The others flocked together in rear of the first, and so — the oiliness of the fat assisting — my bait quickly passed through the entire length of the duck; the second swallowed it, then the third, and so on the rest. At the end of a few minutes, my morsel of fat had traversed the ducks without separating the string; they were strung like pearls by the thread which was passed through their bodies and I returned home.

When, however, I had made good way upon my road, and so large a quantity of ducks proved a great inconvenience, I began to regret that I had so heavy a prize. But in the meantime an event occurred which, at the moment, caused me some anxiety. The ducks were again lively ; little by little, they recovered their first shock, and began to flap their wings, and raise me into the air with them. This was indeed embarrassing. I, however, turned this to my advantage, for, availing myself of the tails of my coat for oars, I guided myself towards my destination. When I arrived at the top of my house, the question was how to come down without injuring myself. I twisted, one after another, the necks of my ducks, and so descended through the flue of the chimney, and, to the great astonishment of my cook, fell into the stove, where, fortunately, there was no fire.

I had another adventure, not unlike the former one, with a lot of partridges. I had come out to try a new gun, and I had just exhausted my supply of small shot, when, unexpectedly, I saw rise at my feet a flock of partridges. The desire to see some of them gracing my table in the evening inspired me with an idea. I reached the place where the flock had settled down; I quickly charged my gun, and, in the place of shot, slipped my ramrod in, allowing the end to protrude beyond the muzzle of the gun. I went towards the partridges. I fired the moment they took their flight; my ramrod went through seven of the birds, who suddenly found themselves, as it were, spitted. How true is the proverb, " Heaven helps those who help themselves ! "

It so happened, on another occasion, that in a fine forest in Russia I came across a splendid black fox, whose skin was of too great value to allow a shot to spoil it. The fox stood close to a tree. In a moment I extracted the ball with which my gun was charged, and in its place put a good spike-nail. I then fired, and hit him so cleverly that I nailed his brush fast to the tree. I immediately went up to him, gave him a cross cut over the face with my hunting-knife, took my whip in hand, and flogged him vigorously until he actually leaped out of his skin.

Chance and good luck often correct our mistakes : of this I had a singular instance soon after, when, in the depth of a forest, I saw a wild pig and sow running close behind each other. My ball had missed them, yet only the foremost pig ran away, and the sow stood motionless, as if fixed to the ground. On examining into the matter, I found the latter one to be an old sow, blind with age, which had taken hold of her pig's tail, in order to be led along by filial duty. My ball having passed between the two, had cut his leading string, which the old sow continued to hold in her mouth ; and as her former guide did not draw her on any longer, she had stopped, of course. I therefore laid hold of the remaining end of the pig's tail, and led the old beast home without any further trouble on my part, and without any reluctance or apprehension on the part of the helpless old animal.

Terrible as these wild sows are, yet more fierce and dangerous are the boars, one of which I had the misfor-

tune to meet in a forest, unprepared for attack or
defence.   I retired behind an oak tree, just when the
furious animal levelled a side blow at me, with such
force, that his tusk pierced through the tree, by which
means he could neither repeat the blow nor retire.   Ho,
ho! thought I, I shall soon have you now ; and immediately I laid hold of a stone, wherewith I hammered,
and bent his tusks in such a manner that he could not
retreat by any means, and must wait my return from
the next village, whither I went for ropes and a cart
to secure him properly, and to carry him off safe and
alive, in which I perfectly succeeded.

You have heard, I dare say, of the hunter's and
sportsman's saint and protector, St. Hubert, and of the
noble stag which appeared to him in the forest, with
the holy cross between his antlers.   I have paid my
homage to that saint every year in good fellowship,
and seen this stag a thousand times, either painted in
churches or embroidered in the stars of his knights ;
so that, upon the honor and conscience of a good sportsman, I hardly know whether there may not have been
formerly, or whether there are not such crossed stags
even at this present day,   But let me rather tell what
I have seen myself.   Having one day spent all my
shot, I found myself unexpectedly in presence of a
stately stag, looking at me as unconcernedly as if he
had known of my empty pouches.   I charged immediately with powder, and upon it a good handful of
cherry-stones, for I had sucked the fruit as far as the
hurry would permit.   Thus I let fly at him, and hit
him just on the middle of the forehead, between his
antlers.   It stunned him, he staggered, yet he made

off. A year or two after, being with a party in the same forest, I beheld a noble stag with a fine full-grown cherry-tree, about ten feet high, between his antlers. I immediately recollected my former adventure, looked upon him as my property, and brought him to the ground by one shot, which at once gave me the haunch and cherry sauce; for the tree was covered with the richest fruit, the like I had never tasted before. Who knows but some passionate, holy sportsman, or sporting abbot, or bishop, may have shot, planted and fixed the cross between the antlers of St. Hubert's stag, in a manner similar to this? They always have been, and still are, famous for plantations of crosses and antlers; and in a case of distress or dilemma, which too often happens to keen sportmen, one is apt to grasp at anything for safety, and to try any expedient, rather than miss the favorable opportunity. I have many times found myself in that trying situation.

What do you say to this, for example? Daylight and powder were spent one day in a Polish forest. When I was going home, a terrible bear made up to me in great speed, with open mouth, ready to fall upon me. All my pockets were searched in an instant for powder and ball, but in vain — I found nothing but two spare flints; one I flung with all my might into the monster's open jaws, down his throat. It gave him pain, and made him turn completely round, so that I could level the second at him also, which, indeed, I did with wonderful success; for it flew in, met the first flint in the stomach, struck fire, and the bear blew up with a terrible explosion. Though I came safe off that time, yet I should not wish to try it again, or venture against bears with no other ammunition.

There is a kind of fatality in it. The fiercest and most dangerous animals generally came upon me when defenceless, as if they had a notion or an instinctive intimation of it. One time it happened, when I unscrewed the flint of my gun to renew it, a huge bear charged upon me with a roar. I was utterly helpless. I could only run to a tree, so as to prepare for my defence. Unfortunately, in climbing, I let my knife fall, and I had nothing to screw in my flint with but my fingers, which were not sufficient. The bear took up his position at the foot of the tree, and every moment I expected to be devoured. As I have related on a previous occasion, I had succeeded in setting fire to my priming with the fire from my eyes, but that expedient did not seem very desirable to me; it had occasioned me a soreness of the eyes, from which I had not again entirely recovered. In despair I contemplated my knife stuck right in the snow. At length, I got an idea as happy as singular. You know from experience that the good hunter, like the philosopher, has always something in readiness. As for me, my game-bag is a regular arsenal, which furnishes me with resources in every crisis. I rummaged, and discovered first a ball of cord, afterwards a piece of bent iron, and then a box full of wax. The wax was hardened by the cold, so I placed it in my bosom to soften it. Then I attached to the cord the piece of iron which I smeared over with plenty of wax, and let it fall immediately to the ground. The piece of iron smeared with the wax, fastened itself to the handle of the knife. Accordingly as the wax grew harder, becoming chilled by the air, it acted as a cement. Having managed so, I manœuvred with care to recover the knife. While I was busily engaged refitting my flint, Master Martin set about ascending the tree, but I met him with such a discharge as relieved him forever of any desire of climbing trees.

Upon another occasion I had a somewhat similar adventure. A frightful wolf rushed upon me so suddenly, and so close, that I could do nothing but follow mechanical instinct, and thrust my fist into his open mouth. For safety's sake I pushed on and on, till my arm was fairly in up to the shoulder. How should I disengage myself? I was not much pleased with my awkward situation — with a wolf face to face, our ogling was not of the most pleasant kind. If I withdrew my arm, then the animal would fly the more furiously upon me; that I saw in his flaming eyes. So, in a moment, I laid hold of his entrails, turned him inside out like a glove, and flung him to the ground, where I left him.

The same expedient would not have answered with a

mad dog, which soon after came running against me in a narrow street at St. Petersburg.

Run who can, I thought; and to do this the better, I threw off my fur cloak, and was safe within doors in an instant. I sent my servant for the cloak, and he put it in the wardrobe with my other clothes. The day after I was amazed and frightened by Jack's brawling, "For God's sake, sir, your fur cloak is mad!" I hastened up to him, and found almost all my clothes tossed about and torn to pieces. The fellow was perfectly right in his apprehensions about the fur cloak's madness. I saw him myself just then falling upon a fine full-dress suit, which he shook and tossed in an unmerciful manner. . . .

Soon after my marriage my wife expressed a desire to join a party in hunting. I went on in advance to try and raise some game, and I had not to wait long before I saw my dog find out some hundreds of partridges. I waited for my wife who was to come after me with my lieutenant and a servant. I waited a long while, but no one came. Finally, rather disturbed, I retraced my path; when, lo! half way along the road, I heard the most wretched groaning. It seemed to be close by; and, meanwhile, I could not discover any signs of a living creature. I dismounted, and placed my ear to the ground, and I soon found that the groans came from beneath the earth. I recognized the voices of my wife, my lieutenant, and the servant. I remembered, on the moment, that they were not far off from the spot where I had opened a shaft for a coal mine; and I had no doubt, alas! that my wife and her companions had been swallowed up. From the nearest village I obtained the assistance of some miners, who, with the most stupendous exertions, succeeded in rescuing the unfortunates from the pit, which was not less than ninety feet in depth. They brought up to the bank the servant and his horse, then the lieutenant and his horse; finally, my wife and her little Barbary horse. The most extraordinary part of the affair is, that notwithstanding this frightful accident, no one — either horse or person — was wounded, with the exception of some insignificant bruises; but they were awfully frightened.

On the following morning I had to leave about a matter of business, and I was detained by it for some days. Immediately on my return, I inquired for my dog Diana, whom I had quite forgotten on the day when we were excited with our adventure. No information could be obtained from my servants, who were in despair of ever seeing her again. A brilliant idea, however, struck me; she is still remaining in guard over the partridges.

I started off at once, full of hope and joy, and, arrived there, what did I see? My dog, motionless, in the selfsame place where I had left her fifteen days before. "Down!" I cried. She dropped her point at once, and put up the partridges, of which I killed twenty-five at a single shot. But the poor creature was so lean and famished, that she had scarce strength enough to come up to me. Indeed, I should never have got her home, had I not taken her up before me on my horse; you can imagine, however, the delight with which I resigned myself to this inconvenience. A few days of rest and care made her as fresh and lively as ever; but some weeks elapsed before I found myself in a position to solve an enigma that, without her aid, would, doubtless, have remained forever incomprehensible to me.

For two days I had been mad after hunting a certain hare. My dog was forever bringing it back to me, but I never could succeed in shooting it. I have seen too many wonderful things to be a believer in witchcraft; but I confess that I felt at my wit's end with that abominable hare. At last I got so close to it, that I could touch it with the muzzle of my gun; it turned head over heels, and what do you think I found? My hare had four feet on the belly, and four others on the back. When the under pair was tired, it turned over, like an agile swimmer who strokes and floats alternately, and started off with renewed vigor on its four fresh feet.

I have never since seen any similar hare, and, assuredly, I should never have taken that one with any other dog than Diana. She was so marvellously superior to all others of her kind that I should assert, without fear of being accused of exaggeration, that she was peerless, had not a greyhound disputed with her the honor of the first place. The greyhound was not so remarkable for her looks as for her incredible swiftness of foot. Had you, gentlemen, seen her, you would, I am sure, have admired her, and not been at all astonished at me for being so fond of her, and taking so much pleasure in hunting with her. This greyhound ran so fast and so long in my service, that she wore her feet down above her ankles, so that in her old age I was able to turn her to good use as a terrier.

I remember this, my wonderful dog, with the same pleasure and tenderness as I do a superb Lithuanian horse, which no money could have bought. He became mine by an accident, which gave me an opportunity of showing my horsemanship to a great advantage. I was at Count Przoboszky's noble country seat in Lithuania, and remained with the ladies at tea in the drawing-room, while the gentlemen went down in the yard, to see a young horse of blood, which had just arrived from the stud. We suddenly heard a noise of distress; I hastened down-stairs, and found the horse so unruly that nobody durst approach or mount him. The most resolute horsemen stood dismayed and aghast; despondency was expressed in every countenance, when, in one leap, I was on his back, took him by surprise, and worked him quite into gentleness and obedience, with the best display of horsemanship I was master of. Fully to show this to the ladies, and save them unnecessary trouble, I forced him to leap in at one of the open windows of the tea-room, walk round several times, pace, trot, and gallop; and at last made him mount the tea-table, there to repeat his lessons in a pretty style of miniature, which was exceedindly pleasing to the ladies, for he performed them amazingly well, and did not break either cup or saucer. It placed me so high in their opinion, and so well in that of the noble lord, that, with his usual politeness, he begged I would accept of this young horse, and ride him full career to conquest and honor, in the campaign against the Turks, which was soon to be opened under the command of Count Munich. . . .

My father told me the following anecdote, which his friends have often heard him relate, and whose truth no one who knew the worthy old man would doubt for a moment: —

"In one of the numerous visits that I paid to England," he said, "I was walking on the sea-shore not far from Harwich. All of a sudden a sea-horse rose out of the waves, and galloped at the top of his speed towards me. I was unarmed, with the exception of my sling. With that, however, I sent two pebbles at him so adroitly that I put out both his eyes. In a trice I jumped on his back, and moved him in the direction of the sea; for his fierceness had departed with his eyes, and he let himself be guided as quietly as a lamb. I slipped my sling into his mouth as a bridle, and thus accoutred I stood out to sea.

"In less than three hours we had reached the opposite shore: in that space of time we had traversed a distance of thirty miles. At Helvoetsluys I sold my nag for seven hundred ducats to mine host of the Three Cups. He exhibited the wonderful creature at so much a head, and made a pretty fortune out of him. You can read his description in Buffon. But, however extraordinary that method of travelling might be " — my father used to add — " the observations and discoveries I was enabled to make thereby are more extraordinary still.

" The animal I rode did not swim; he galloped with incredible swiftness along the bottom of the sea, driving before him millions of fish, quite different from those one is in the habit of seeing. Some of them had their heads in the middle of their bodies, others at the end of their tails; some, standing in a circle sang choruses of inexpressible beauty; others were engaged in building transparent palaces of water, surrounded by vast colonnades, through which rippled to and fro a clear shining fluid, resembling the most brilliant fire. The interior of these buildings was provided with every convenience that could suit fish of distinction; there were nurseries for the safe keeping of the spawn; a suite of spacious halls was devoted to the education of the young fish. The method of instruction — as far as I could judge of it by what I saw, for their words were as unintelligible to me as the song of the birds or the dialogue of the grasshoppers — appeared to me to resemble so closely that which is employed at present in charitable institutions upon earth, that I felt persuaded that one of our theorists had made a journey similar to mine, and fished his ideas out of the water instead of catching them in

the air. In general, you will conclude from what I
have just told you, that there is still in the world a
vast field of investigation that well deserves to be ex-
plored and studied. But I must go on with my
story.

"Among other incidents of travel, I crossed a vast
range of mountains, as lofty, at the very least, as the
Alps. Among the clefts of the rocks a forest of tall
trees of various kinds was growing, to whose branches
clung lobsters, crabs, oysters, mussels, and sea-snails of
so vast a size that a single one would have been a
load for a wagon, and the smallest would have crushed
a porter. All the individuals of this kind that are cast
up on our shores, and sold in our markets, are mere
poverty-stricken creatures that the water washes off the
branches, exactly as the wind shakes unripe-fruit off a
tree. The trees on which the lobsters lived seemed to
me to bear the most fruit; but those belonging to crabs
and oysters were the largest. The little sea-snails grow
on a sort of a shrub which is nearly always to be found
growing at the foot of the crab-trees, and climbs up
them, as ivy does over an oak.

" When I had got about half way across, I found myself in a valley situated at least five hundred fathoms
beneath the surface of the sea. I began to suffer from
want of air. Besides, my situation was far from agreeable for other reasons. I met, from time to time, with
huge fishes, which, as far as I could judge from the
formidable way in which they opened their throats,
seemed not altogether unwilling to swallow up both of
us. My poor Rozinante could not see: so I had only
my own good sense to help me in escaping from the

hostile intentions of these hungry gentlemen. I therefore galloped on without stopping, so as to reach dry land as soon as possible, and finally arrived at the Dutch coast at Helvoetsluys."

Here my father's narrative generally came to an end.

AN EXPERIMENT IN CHANGING COLORS

(FROM TEN THOUSAND A YEAR.)

BY SAMUEL WARREN.

MR. Tittlebat Titmouse, a poor clerk in Mr. Tag-rag's dry goods store, was a young gentleman with "abominable sandy-colored hair," and spreading whiskers, curling out on each side of his chin above his stock "like two little horns or tusks." He suddenly came into a fortune, which it was his first desire to spend upon his personal appearance.]

Titmouse, for the remainder of the day, felt, as may be imagined, but little at his ease; for — to say nothing of his insuperable repugnance to the discharge of any of his former duties; his uneasiness under the oppressing civilities of Mr. Tag-rag; and the evident disgust towards him entertained by his companions; many most important considerations arising out of recent and coming events — his altering circumstances — were momentarily forcing themselves upon his attention.

The first of these was his *hair ;* for Heaven seemed to have suddenly given him the long-coveted means of changing its detested hue; and the next was *an eye-glass,* without which, he had long felt his appearance and appointments to be painfully incomplete. Early in the afternoon, therefore, on the readily-admitted plea of important business, he obtained the permission of the obsequious Mr. Tag-rag to depart for the day, and instantly directed his steps to the well-known shop of a fashionable perfumer and perruquier, in Bond Street — well known to those, at least, who were in the habit of glancing at the enticing advertisements in the newspapers.

Having watched through the window till the coast was clear (for he felt a natural delicacy in asking for a hair dye before people who could in an instant perceive his urgent occasion for it,) he entered the shop, where a well dressed gentleman was sitting behind the counter reading. He was handsome; and his elaborately curled hair was of a heavenly black (so at least Titmouse considered it) that was better than a thousand printed advertisements of the celebrated fluid which formed the chief commodity there vended.

Titmouse, with a little hesitation, asked this gentleman what was the price of their article " for turning *light* hair black " — and was answered — " only seven and sixpence for the smaller-sized bottle."

One was in a twinkling placed upon the counter, where it lay like a miniature mummy, swathed, as it were, in manifold advertisements.

" You'll find the fullest directions within, and testi-

monials from the highest nobility to the wonderful
efficacy of the ' CYANOCHAITANTHROPOPOION. ' " [1]

"*Sure* it will do, sir?" inquired Titmouse anxiously.

"Is *my* hair dark enough to your taste, sir?" said
the gentleman, with a calm and bland manner —
"because I owe it entirely to this valuable specific."

"Do you, indeed, sir?" inquired Titmouse: adding
with a sigh, "but, between ourselves look at mine!" —
and, lifting off his hat for a moment, he exhibited a
great crop of bushy, carroty hair.

"Whew! rather ugly that, sir!" exclaimed the
gentleman, looking very serious — "What a curse to be
born with such hair, isn't it?"

"'Pon my life I think so, sir!" answered Titmouse
mournfully; "and do you really say, sir, that this
what's-its-name turned yours of that beautiful black?"

"Think? 'Pon my honor, sir, — certain; no mistake,
I assure you! I was fretting myself into my grave
about the color of my hair! Why, sir, there was a nobleman in here (I don't like to mention names) the other
day, with a head that seemed as if it had been dipped
into water, and then powdered with brick dust; but —
I assure you, the Cyanochaitanthropopoion was too
much for it — it turned black in a very short time.
You should have seen his lordship's ecstasy — [the
speaker saw that Titmouse would swallow anything;

[1] This fearful looking word, I wish to inform my lady readers, is an
original and monstrous amalgamation of three or four Greek words —
κυανοχαιτανθρωποποιῶν — denoting a fluid "*that can render the human
hair black.*" Whenever a barber or perfumer determines on trying to
puff off some villanous imposition of this sort, strange to say, he goes
to some starving scholar, and gives him half-a-crown to coin a word like
the above, that shall be equally unintelligible and unpronounceable, and
therefore attractive and popular.

so he went on with a confident air] — and in a month's time he had married a beautiful woman whom he had loved from a child, but who had vowed she could never bring herself to marry a man with such a head of hair."

" How long does it take to do all this, sir?" interrupted Titmouse eagerly, with a beating heart.

"Sometimes two — sometimes three days. In four days' time, I'll answer for it, your most intimate friend would not know you. My wife did not know me for a long while, and wouldn't let me salute her — ha, ha!"

Here another customer entered; and Titmouse laying down the five-pound note he had squeezed out of Tagrag, put the wonder-working phial into his pocket, and on receiving his change, departed, bursting with eagerness to try the effects of the Cyanochaitanthropopoion.

Within half an hour's time he might have been seen driving a hard bargain with a pawnbroker, for a massive-looking eye-glass, which, as it hung suspended in the window, he had for months cast a longing eye upon; and he eventually purchased it (his eyesight, I need hardly say, was perfect) for only fifteen shillings. After taking a hearty dinner in a little dusky eating-house in Rupert Street, frequented by fashionable looking foreigners, with splendid heads of curling hair and mustaches, he hastened home, eager to commence the grand experiment. Fortunately, he was undisturbed that evening.

Having lit his candle, and locked his door, with tremulous fingers he opened the papers enveloping the little phial; and glancing over their contents, got so inflamed with the numberless instances of its efficacy, detailed in brief but glowing terms — as — the " Duke of . . . . . . — the Countess of . . . . . . — the Earl of, etc. — the lovely Miss ———, the celebrated Sir Little Bull's-eye (who was so gratified that he allowed his name to be used), — all of whom, from having hair of the reddest possible description, were now possessed of raven-hued locks "— that he threw down the paper, and hurriedly got the cork out of the bottle.

Having turned up his coat cuffs he commenced the application of the Cyanochaitanthropopoion, rubbing it into his hair, eyebrows, and whiskers, with all the energy he was capable of, for upwards of half an hour. Then he read over again every syllable on the papers in which the phial had been wrapped; and about eleven o'clock, having given sundry curious glances at the glass, got into bed, full of exciting hopes and delightful anxieties concerning the success of the great experiment he was trying.

He could not sleep for several hours. He dreamed a rapturous dream — that he bowed to a gentleman with coal-black hair, whom he fancied he had seen before — and suddenly discovered that he was only looking at *himself* in a glass ! ! — This woke him. Up he jumped — sprung to his little glass breathlessly — but ah ! merciful Heavens ! he almost dropped down dead ! His hair was perfectly *green* — there could be no mistake about it. He stood there staring in the glass in speechless horror, his eyes and mouth distended to their utmost for several minutes. Then he threw himself on the bed, and felt fainting. Up he presently jumped again in a kind of ecstasy — rubbed his hair desperately and wildly about — again looked into the glass — there it was, rougher than before; but eyebrows, whiskers, and head — all were, if anything, of a more vivid and brilliant green.

Despair came over him. What had all his past troubles been to this? — what was to become of him? He got into bed again and burst into a perspiration. Two or three times he got into and out of bed, to look at himself again — on each occasion deriving only more terrible confirmation than before of the disaster that had befallen him. After lying still for some minutes, he got out of bed and kneeling down, tried to say his prayers; but it was in vain — and he rose half choked. It was plain that he must have his head shaved, and wear a wig — that was making an old man of him at once. Getting more and more disturbed in his mind, he dressed himself, half determined on starting off to Bond Street, and breaking every pane of glass in the shop window of the cruel impostor who had sold him the liquid that had so frightfully disfigured him. As he stood thus irresolute, he heard the step of Mrs. Squallop (his landlady) approaching his door, and recollected that he had ordered her to bring up his tea-kettle about that time.

Having no time to take his clothes off, he thought the best thing he could do would be to pop into bed again, draw his nightcap down to his ears and eyebrows, pretend to be asleep, and, turning his back towards the door, have chance of escaping the observation of his landlady. No sooner thought of than done. Into bed he jumped, and drew the clothes over him — not aware, however, that in his hurry he had left his legs, with boots and trousers exposed to view — an unusual spectacle to his landlady, who had, in fact, scarcely ever known him in bed at so late an hour before. He lay as still as a mouse.

Mrs. Squallop, after glancing with surprise at his legs, happening to direct her eyes toward the window, beheld a small phial, only half of whose dark contents were remaining — oh gracious! — of course it must be POISON, and Mr. Titmouse must be dead! — In a sudden fright she dropped the kettle, plucked the clothes off the trembling Titmouse, and cried out, — "Oh, Mr. Titmouse! Mr. Titmouse! what *have* you been" —

"Well, ma'am, what the deuce do you mean? How dare" — commenced Titmouse, suddenly sitting up, and looking furiously at Mrs. Squallop. An inconceivably strange and horrid figure he looked. He had all his day clothes on; a white cotton nightcap was drawn down to his very eyes, like a man going to be hanged; his face was very pale, and his whiskers were of a bright green color.

"Lard a-mighty!" exclaimed Mrs. Squallop, faintly, the moment that this strange apparition presented itself; and, sinking on the chair, she pointed with a dismayed air to the ominous-looking object standing on the window-shelf. Titmouse from that supposed she had found out the true state of the case.

"Well — *isn't* it an infernal shame, Mrs. Squallop?" said he getting off the bed, and plucking off his night-cap, exhibited the full extent of his misfortune. "What d'ye think of *that!*" he exclaimed, staring wildly at her. Mrs. Squallop gave a faint shriek, turned her head aside, and motioned him away.

" I shall go mad — I SHALL ! " cried Titmouse, tearing his green hair.

" Oh Lord ! — oh Lord ! " groaned Mrs. Squallop, evidently expecting him to leap upon her. Presently, however, she a little recovered her presence of mind ; and Titmouse, stuttering with fury, explained to her what had taken place. As he went on, Mrs. Squallop became less and less able to control herself, and at length burst into a fit of convulsive laughter, and sat holding her hands to her fat, shaking sides, as if she would have tumbled off her chair. Titmouse was almost on the point of striking her ! At length, however, the fit went off ; and, wiping her eyes, she expressed the greatest commiseration for him, and proposed to go down and fetch up some soft soap and flannel, and try what a good hearty wash would do.

Scarce sooner said than done — but, alas, in vain. Scrub, scrub — lather, lather, did they both ; but, the instant the soap-suds were washed off, there was the head as green as ever !

" Oh murder, murder ! what *am* I to do, Mrs. Squallop ? " groaned Titmouse, having taken another look at himself in the glass.

" Why — really I'd be off to a police-office, and have 'em all taken up, if as how I was *you !* " quoth Mrs. Squallop.

" No — See if I don't take that bottle, and make the fellow that sold it me swallow what's left — and I'll smash in his shop front besides ! "

" Oh you won't — you mustn't — not on no account ! Stop at home a bit, and be quiet ; it may go off with all this washing, in the course of the day. Soft soap is an

uncommon strong thing for getting colors out — but —
a — a — excuse me, Mr. Titmouse — why wasn't you
satisfied with the hair God Almighty had given you?
D'ye think He didn't know a deal better than you what
was best for you? I'm blest if I don't think this is a
judgment on you."

"What's the use of your standing preaching to me
in this way, Mrs. Squallop?" said Titmouse, first with
amazement, and then with fury in his manner — " A'n't
I half mad without it? Judgment or no judgment —
where's the harm of my wanting black hair any more
than black trousers? That a'n't *your own* hair, Mrs.
Squallop — you're as gray as a badger underneath —
'pon my soul! I've often remarked it."

"I'll tell you what, Mr. himperance!" furiously
exclaimed Mrs. Squallop, "you're no gentleman! And
you deserve what you've got! It *is* a judgment, and I
hope it will stick by you — so take *that* for sauce, you
vulgar fellow!" (snapping her fingers at him). "Get
rid of your green hair if you can! It's only carrot
tops instead of carrot *roots* — and some likes one,
some the other — ha! ha! ha!"

"I'll tell you what, Mrs. Squ——" he commenced,
but she had gone, having slammed to the door behind
her with all her force; and Titmouse was left alone in
a half frantic state, in which he continued for nearly
two hours. Once again he read over the atrocious
puffs which had overnight inflated him to such a degree, and he now saw that they were all lies. This is
a sample of them : —

"This divine fluid (as it was enthusiastically styled
to the inventor, by the lovely Duchess of Doodle)

possesses the inestimable and astonishing quality of changing hair, of whatever color, to a dazzling jet black; at the same time imparting to it a rich glossy appearance, which wonderfully contributes to the imposing *tout ensemble* presented by those who use it. That well-known ornament of the circle of fashion, the young and lovely Mrs. Fitzfrippery, owned to the proprietor that to this surprising fluid it was that she was indebted for those unrivalled raven ringlets which attracted the eyes of envying and admiring crowds," and so forth.   A little further on : — "This exquisite effect is not *in all cases* produced instantaneously; much will of course depend (as the celebrated M. Dupuytren, of the Hotel Dieu, at Paris, informed the inventor) on the physical idiosyncrasy of the party using it, with reference to the constituent particles of the coloring matter constituting the fluid in the capillary vessels.   Often a single application suffices to change the most hopeless-looking head of red hair to as deep a black; but not unfrequently the hair *passes through intermediate shades and tints* — all, however, ultimately settling into a deep and permanent black."

This passage not a little revived the drooping spirits of Titmouse.   Accidentally, however, an asterisk at the last word in the above sentence, directed his eye to a note at the bottom of the page, printed in such minute type as baffled any but the strongest sight and most determined eye to read, and which said note was the following : —

"Though cases *do*, undoubtedly, occasionally occur, in which the native inherent indestructible qualities of the hair defy all attempts at change or even modification, and resist even *this* potent remedy : of which, however, in all his experience " (the wonderful specific has been invented for about *six months*) " the inventor has known but very few instances." But to this exceedingly select class of unfortunate incurables, poor Titmouse, alas! entertained a dismal suspicion that *he* belonged!

"Look, sir! Look! Only look here what your wretched stuff has done to my hair!" said Titmouse, on presenting himself soon after to the gentleman who had sold him the infernal liquid; and, taking off his hat, exposed his green hair. The gentleman, however, did not appear at all surprised or discomposed.

"Look, Sir! Look!"

"Ah — yes! I see — I see. You're in the intermediate stage. It differs in different people — "

"Differs, sir! I'm going mad! I look like a green monkey."

"In *me*, now, the color was a strong *yellow*. But, have you read the explanations that are given in the wrapper?"

"Read 'em?" echoed Titmouse furiously — "I should think so! Much good they do *me*! Sir, you're a humbug! — an impostor! I'm a sight to be seen for the rest of my life! Look at me, sir! Eyebrows, whiskers, and all!"

"*Rather* a singular appearance, just at present, I must own," said the gentleman, his face turning suddenly red all over with the violent effort he was making to prevent an explosion of laughter. He soon, however, recovered himself, and added coolly — " If you'll only persevere — "

"Persevere!" interrupted Titmouse, violently clapping his hat on his head, "I'll teach you to persevere in taking in the public! I'll have a warrant out against you in no time!"

"Oh, my dear sir, I'm accustomed to all this!" said the gentleman coolly.

"You—are—what?" gasped Titmouse, quite aghast.

"Oh, often—often, while the liquid is performing the first stage of the change; but, in a day or two afterwards, the parties generally come back smiling into my shop, with heads as black as crows!"

"No! But really—do they, sir?" interrupted Titmouse, drawing a long breath.

"Hundreds, I may say thousands, my dear sir! And one lady gave me a picture of herself, in her black hair, to make up for her abuse of me when it was a puce color — Fact, honor!"

"But do you recollect anyone's hair turning green, and then getting black?" inquired Titmouse with trembling anxiety.

"Recollect any? Fifty, at least. For instance, there was Lord Albert Addlehead — but why should I name names? I know hundreds! But everything is honor and confidential *here!*"

"And did Lord what's-his-name's hair go green, and then black? and was it at first as light as mine?"

"His hair was redder, and in consequence it became greener, and now is blacker than ever yours will be."

" Well, if I and my landlady have this morning used an ounce, we've used a quarter of a pound of soft soap in " —

" Soft soap ! — soft soap ! " cried out the gentleman with an air of sudden alarm — " that explains all " (he forgot how well it had already been explained by him).   " By Heavens, sir ! — soft soap !   You may have ruined your hair forever ! "   Titmouse opened his eyes and mouth with a start of terror, it not occurring to his reflecting mind that the intolerable green had preceded and caused, not followed, the use of the soft soap. " Go home, my dear sir !   God bless you — go home, as you value your hair ; take this small bottle of DAMASCUS CREAM, and rub it in before it's too late; and then use the remainder of the " —

" Then you don't think it's already too late ? " inquired Titmouse faintly ; and having been assured to the contrary — having asked the price of the Damascus cream, which was " *only* three-and-sixpence," (stamp included) — he paid it with a rueful air, and took his departure.   He sneaked along the streets with the air of a pick-pocket, fearful that everyone he met was an officer who had his eye on him.   He was not, in fact, very far off the mark ; for many a person smiled, and stared, and turned round to look at him as he went along.

Titmouse slunk up-stairs to his room in a sad state of depression, and spent the next hour in rubbing into his hair the Damascus cream.   He rubbed till he could hardly hold his arms up any longer, from sheer fatigue. Having risen at length to mark, from the glass, the progress he had made, he found that the only result of his persevering exertions had been to give a greasy,

shining appearance to the hair, that remained as green
as ever. With a half-uttered groan he sunk down upon
a chair, and fell into a sort of abstraction, which was
interrupted by a sharp knock at his door.

Titmouse started up, trembled, and stood for a moment or two irresolute, glancing fearfully at the glass;
and then, opening the door, let in Mr. Gammon, who
started back a pace or two, as if he had been shot, on
catching sight of the strange figure of Titmouse.

It was useless for Gammon to try to check his
laughter; so, leaning against the door-post, he yielded
to the impulse, and laughed without intermission for
at least two minutes. Titmouse felt desperately angry,
but feared to show it; and the timid, rueful, lackadaisi-
cal air with which he regarded the dreaded Mr. Gammon, only prolonged and aggravated the agonies of
that gentleman.

When at length he had a little recovered himself,
holding his left hand to his side, with an exhausted air,
he entered the little apartment, and asked Titmouse
what in the name of Heaven he had been doing to himself: *" Without this "* (in the absurd slang of the
lawyers) that he suspected most vehemently all the
while quite well what Titmouse had been about; but
he wished to hear Titmouse's own account of the
matter! — Titmouse, not daring to hesitate, complied
— Gammon listening in an agony of suppressed laughter. He looked as little at Titmouse as he could, and
was growing a trifle more sedate, when Titmouse, in a
truly lamentable tone, inquired, " What's the good, Mr.
Gammon, of ten thousand a-year with such a horrid
head of hair as this? ". . .

As Gammon bent his steps towards Saffron Hill, he reflected rather anxiously on several matters that had occurred to him during the interview which I have just described. On reaching the office, he was presently closeted with Mr. Quirk, to whom, first and foremost, he exhibited and delivered the documents to which he had obtained Titmouse's signature.

"Now, Gammon," said the old gentleman, as soon as he had locked up in his safe the above-mentioned documents — "Now, Gammon, I think we may be up and at 'em; load our guns, and blaze away," and he rubbed his hands.

"Perhaps so, Mr. Quirk," replied Gammon; "but we must, for no earthly consideration, be premature in our operations! Let me, by the way, tell you one or two little matters that have just occurred to Titmouse!" — Then he told Mr. Quirk of the effects which had followed the use of the potent Cyanochaitanthropopoion, at which old Quirk almost laughed himself into fits. When, however, Gammon, with a serious air, mentioned the name of Miss Tag-rag, and his grave suspicions concerning her, Quirk bounced up out of his chair, almost startling Gammon out of *his*. If he had just been told that his banker had broke, he could scarce have shown more emotion. . . .

When Titmouse rose the next morning (Saturday), behold! — he found his hair had become of a variously shaded purple or violet color! Astonishment and apprehension by turns possessed him, as he stared into the glass, at this unlooked-for change of color; and hastily dressing himself, after swallowing a very slight breakfast, off he went once more to the scientific establish-

ment in Bond Street, to which he had been indebted for
his recent delightful experiences. The distinguished
inventor and proprietor of the Cyanochaitanthropopoion
was behind the counter as usual — calm and confident
as ever.

" Ah! I see — as I said! as I said! " quoth he, with a
sort of glee in his manner. " Isn't it? — coming round
quicker than usual. — Really, I'm selling more of the
article than I can possibly make."

" Well," — at length said Titmouse, as soon as he had
recovered from the surprise occasioned by the the sudden volubility with which he had been assailed on entering — " then *is* it really going on tolerable well? "
taking off his hat, and looking anxiously into a glass
that hung close by.

" *Tolerable* well, my dear sir! Delightful! Perfect!
Couldn't be better! If you'd studied the thing, you'd
know, sir, that purple is the middle color between green
and black. Indeed, black's only purple and green
mixed, which explains the whole thing! "

Titmouse listened with infinite satisfaction to this
philosophical statement.

" Remember, sir — my hair is to come like yours —
eh? you recollect, sir? Honor — that was the bargain,
you know! "

" I have very little doubt of it, sir — nay, I am certain of it, knowing it by experience."

[The scamp had been hired expressly for the purpose
of lying thus in support of the Cyanochaitanthropopoion,
his own hair being a natural black.]

" I'm going to a great dinner to-morrow, sir " said
Titmouse, " with some terrible great people, at the west

end of the town — eh? you understand? Will it do by
that time? Would give a trifle to get my hair a shade
darker by that time — for — hem! — most lovely girl
— eh? you understand the thing? — terrible anxious,
and all that sort of thing, you know!"

"Yes — I do," replied the gentleman of the shop, in
a confidential tone; and opening one of the glass doors
behind him, took out a bottle considerably larger than
the first, and handed it to Titmouse. "This," said he,
"will complete the thing; it combines chemically with
the purple particles, and the result is — generally arrived at in about two days' time —

"But it will do *something* in a night's time — eh?
— surely."

"I should think so! But here it is — it is called
the TETARAGMENON ABRACADABRA."

"What a name!" exclaimed Titmouse with a kind
of awe. "'Pon honor, it almost takes one's breath
away —"

"It will do more, sir; it will take your red hair
away! By the way, only the day before yesterday, a
lady of high rank (between ourselves, Lady Caroline
Carrot), whose red hair always seemed as if it would
have set her bonnet in a blaze — ha, ha! — came here,
after two days' use of the Cyanochaitanthropopoion,
and one day's use of this Tetaragmenon Abracadabra —
and asked me if I knew her. Upon my soul I did not,
till she solemnly assured me she was really Lady Caroline!"

"*How* much is it?" eagerly inquired Titmouse,
thrusting his hand into his pocket, with no little excitement.

" Only nine-and-sixpence."

" Oh, my stars, what a price! Nine-and-six — "

" Ah, but would you have believed it, sir? This extraordinary fluid cost a great German chemist his whole life to bring to perfection; and it contains expensive materials from all the four corners of the world!"

" That may be — but really — I've laid out a large figure with you, sir, this day or two! Couldn't you say eight sh — ?"

" We never abate, sir; it is not *our* style of doing business," replied the gentleman, in a manner that quite overawed poor Titmouse, who at once bought this, the third abomination; not a little depressed, however, at the heavy prices he had paid for the three bottles, and the uncertainty he felt as to the ultimate issue. That night, he was so well satisfied with the progress which the hair on his head was making (for, by candlelight, it really looked much darker than could have been expected), that he resolved — at all events for the present — to leave well alone; or at the utmost, to try the effects of the Tetaragmenon Abracadabra only upon his eyebrows and whiskers.

Into them he rubbed the new specific; which on the bottle being opened, surprised him in two respects: first, it was perfectly colorless; secondly, it had a most infernal smell. However, it was no use hesitating: he had bought and paid for it; and the papers it was folded in gave an account of its success that was really irresistible and unquestionable. Away, therefore, he rubbed; and when he had finished, got into bed, in humble hope as to the result which would be disclosed by the morning's light. But, alas! would you have believed it? When he looked at himself in the glass, about six o'clock (at which hour he awoke), I protest it is a fact, that his eyebrows and whiskers were as white as snow ; which combining with the purple color of the hair on his head, rendered him one of the most astounding objects (in human shape) the eye of man had ever beheld. There was the wisdom of age seated in his eyebrows and whiskers, unspeakable youthful folly in his features, and a purple crown of WONDER on his head.

Really, it seemed as if the devil were wreaking his spite on Mr. Titmouse; nay, perhaps it was the devil himself who had served him with the bottles in Bond Street. Or was it a mere ordinary servant of the devil — some greedy, impudent, unprincipled speculator, who, desirous of acting on the approved maxim — *Fiat experimentum in corpore vili* — had pitched on Titmouse (seeing the sort of person he was) as a godsend, quite reckless what effect he produced on his hair, so as the stuff was paid for, and its effects noted? It might possibly have been sport to the gentleman of the shop, but it was near proving death to poor Titmouse, who really might have resolved on throwing himself out of the window, only that he saw it was not big enough for a baby to get through.

He turned aghast at the monstrous object which his little glass presented to him ; and sunk down upon the bed with a feeling as if he were now fit for death. As before, Mrs. Squallop made her appearance with his kettle for breakfast. He was sitting at the table dressed, and with his arms folded, with a reckless air, not at all caring to conceal the new and still more frightful change which he had undergone since she saw him last. Mrs. Squallop stared at him for a second or two in silence: then, stepping back out of the room,

suddenly drew to the door and stood outside, laughing vehemently.

"I'll kick you down-stairs!" shouted Titmouse, rushing to the door, pale with fury, and pulling it open.

"Mr. — Mr. — Titmouse, you'll be the death of me — you will — you will!" gasped Mrs. Squallop, almost black in the face, and the water running out of the kettle, which she was unconsciously holding in a slant.

After a while, however, they got reconciled. Mrs. Squallop, had fancied he had been but rubbing chalk on his eyebrows and whiskers; and seemed dismayed, indeed, on hearing the true state of the case. He implored her to send out for a small bottle of ink; but as it was Sunday morning none could be got; and she teased him to try a little blacking! He did — but, of course, it was useless.

"I'll Kick You Down-Stairs."

He sat for an hour or two in an ecstasy of grief and rage. What would he now have given never to have meddled with the hair which Heaven had thought fit to send him into the world with? Alas! with what mournful force Mrs. Squallop's words again and again recurred to him! To say that he ate breakfast would be scarcely correct. He drank a single cup of cocoa, and ate about three inches length and thickness of a roll, and then put away his breakfast things on the window shelf. If he had been in the humor to go to church, how could he? He would have been turned out as an object involuntarily inciting everybody to laughter.

TILL OWLGLASS

INTRODUCTION.

IT has always been customary in relating the biography of a celebrated man to begin with his birth, but in order to have the story of Till Owlglass in keeping with his life, the historian must commence with the death of his hero. For he never did as other people did, but was ever an odd genius. Beside the story of his comical sayings and doings, a rusty dagger and an old iron spectacle frame are the only relics once belonging to the famous jester which have been handed down to posterity.

In the Duchy of Lauenburg, near a lovely lake overshadowed by beech woods, lies the grave of Till Owlglass. Even his headstone is different from other monuments to the dead, which usually have inscribed upon them that such and such a one *lies* buried; for on the stone that marks his resting-place are engraved the following lines :

> " Touch not this stone with ruthless hands,
> For buried here Till Owlglass stands.
> Anno Domini MCCCL."

As no one can be buried who never existed, the epitaph proves that a Till Owlglass must actually have lived. Furthermore, the singular wording of the inscription, which states that here *stands*, instead of here *lies*, the one buried beneath, shows what an unusual and remarkable man he must have been.

His merry pranks are well worth being told again and again; for the sad events of life are so numerous, and the laughable ones so few, that his jokes and jests not only afford pleasure, but many times contain a moral. For in the nonsense of Germany's favorite fool there was often more wisdom than in other people's sense.

Till reached out in the dark and gave a vigorous tug to
the first thief's hair.

TILL OWLGLASS' FUNNY PRANKS

(TILL EULENSPIEGEL.)

DONE INTO ENGLISH FOR THE YOUNG FOLKS BY

JULIA ISABEL BULL.

TILL'S BOYHOOD.

N a fine old castle on the banks of the Rhine, there
once lived a valiant Duke who was also a mighty
robber. He was so famous for his daring deeds,
that he was the wonder of all the neighborhood.
In fact, one worthy man, named Owlglass, living
in a little village nearby, admired him so greatly, that
he asked the noble lord to be his little son's godfather.
This the bold highwayman consented to do, giving the
child at baptism his own name, Till. This curious name,
however, was not more remarkable than the career of
him who received it, as you shall hear. Scarcely had
he been baptized when his adventures began. On the
way home from church, the woman who carried him
lost her balance, in crossing a little foot-bridge, and fell,
baby and all, into the muddy water below. Fortunately
the rest of the company quickly dragged them out, and
placed them upon dry land. Thus little Till, when but
three days old, narrowly escaped a wretched death upon
his very first journey. Reaching home, safe and sound,
but sadly dirty, young Till was placed in a tub of warm
water, and washed clean and fresh once more. He had
the strange experience of being baptized three times in

one day — once at church, then in the stream, and finally in the wash tub.

When Till Owlglass was old enough to walk alone he often played with other children, and tumbled about and turned sommersaults in the grass just like other boys. Every one thought him a very good child, and never dreamed of the roguishness that was in him, but he was hardly six years old before he began to show how full of pranks he was.

On his way to school one day, Till met the Duke, who, pleased with the boy's bright face, stopped to talk with him.

"Where are you going, my little man?" asked the Duke.

"To school," the lad replied.

"Take this dollar and buy yourself some candy."

"That would be foolish," cried Till. "My father would see me eating it, and ask where the money for candy came from. He would not believe that any one had given it me, and would beat me."

"Take the dollar," urged the Duke, "and if your father asks who gave it to you, tell him it was the Duke himself."

"Father will not believe me," said Till.

"And why not, my son?" asked the Duke.

"Did a Duke ever give but one dollar?" asked little Till. "You must fill my school-bag with dollars, then I shall be believed."

"You are right, my lad," answered the Duke laughing. He filled Till's bag with dollars, and said: "Now go home and show your father your treasure, and he will readily believe that the Duke himself has made you a present."

" Who honored as a Prince would be,
Must with his gold be ever free."

One day Till's mother took him to a neighboring village to attend a church festival. After a day of pleasure at the fair, Till became tired, and toward evening sought a suitable place for a quiet nap. He discovered behind a farmhouse a row of bee-hives. Creeping into an empty one, he needed no rocking to put him to sleep. His mother, supposing he had run on ahead, went home late in the evening.

During the night two thieves came to steal some of the honey, and one of them said: "I have always heard that the heaviest bee-hives have the best honey."

"True," answered the other, "we will choose the heaviest." So they lifted the hives, one after the other, and as they came to the one in which Owlglass slept, said: "This must be the best one." So they picked it up and carried it off.

Before long Till woke up and heard the thieves talking and chuckling over the prize they had gotten. Till reached out in the dark, and gave a vigorous tug to the first thief's hair. He, thinking his companion had pulled it, scolded him heartily, but the second thief cried: "You must be dreaming, Sleepyhead! How can I pull your hair when it takes both hands to carry this heavy hive?" Owlglass laughed in his sleeve, enjoying the fun, and after they had gone some yards further, played the same trick on the man behind him, who cried out angrily to his companion to let him alone. Till kept on pulling the hair, first of one rogue and then of the other, until finally, seizing each by a lock in the nape of the neck, he tugged with all his might.　This made the thieves so furious, that they dropped the bee-hive and pounded each other with their fists.　In the midst of the combat Till crept out and ran away. . . .

TILL AT THE FARM.

ILL'S mother was so unhappy because her son showed no desire to earn his living, that she finally took the matter into her own hands and hired him out to a farmer as man of all work.　The very first thing that Owlglass' master bade him to do was to go to town and buy a pair of little pigs at the market.　Till did as he was told, put the tiny pigs in a bag, and asked a teamster whom he met at the market if he might put the bag in his wagon.　The teamster said: "Yes."　So Owlglass lost no time in throwing his bag of pigs into the wagon and then wandered off seeking amusement. A cart loaded with ripe plums first attracted his atten-tion.　Without so much as saying, "By your leave," he stopped before the cart and began to devour the luscious fruit.

"Here, fellow, what are you doing?" cried the fruit seller.

"You can see for yourself, I am eating plums," an-swered Till, coolly.

This was too much for the fruit vender, so without wasting any more words he began to beat Owlglass with a stick, who, without allowing himself to be dis-turbed by the blows, went on with his feast, to the great amusement of the bystanders.　At last, when Till could eat no more, he said to the crowd about him:

"This is a fine market, where people are forced by blows to eat plums whether they wish to or not."

While this was going on the teamster was busy loading his wagon with bales and boxes, and he piled them on top of Till's bag, not knowing what was inside.

When his wagon was full, the teamster and Owlglass climbed upon the seat, and drove merrily home. When Till opened his bag to show his master the pigs the poor little things were dead! The farmer scolded him severely, and said: "You should have driven them home before you. See that you do it the next time I send you to buy anything."

"I will remember," answered Owlglass.

Till's next errand to the market was to buy a bag of peas. He had carried them to the top of the mountain before it occurred to him that his master had told him to drive his next purchase home before him. He quickly emptied the bag so that the peas rolled merrily down the hill, Till, with the empty bag, following at his leisure. The farmer no sooner caught sight of him than he cried: "Till, where are the peas?"

"They will soon be here," answered Owlglass. "I poured them out of the bag at the top of the mountain, and they rolled so nimbly down hill that I did not even have to drive them."

At this the farmer became so angry that he cried: "You fool; you should have tied up the bag with a string and hung it over your back."

"I will remember," answered Owlglass.

When Till was next sent to market it was to buy a young goat, so he tied a string about its neck and slung it over his shoulder, so that the poor animal soon choked to death. Upon reaching home the farmer boxed him soundly on the ear, besides giving him the usual scolding. "Why didn't you lead the goat home, instead of hanging him like a thief on the gallows?"

"I will remember," answered Owlglass.

Soon after he was sent to market again, this time to buy earthen pots for the kitchen. The handles of these he tied to a string, and dragged them along behind him, the pots, as you have already guessed, being smashed to pieces, and the fragments strewing the pathway behind him. The farmer flew into a rage, beat Till with a club and sent him away.

In spite of this bad ending to his first experience as a farm hand, Till soon hired himself to another farmer. His new master took him to the forest, to get a load of wood, for he wished to build a barn. As they drove away, a hare sprang across the road, and the farmer said: "Turn back, Till; a hare has crossed our path, and that means bad luck for to-day. We won't go for the wood until to-morrow." So they turned about, and did not start out again until the next day. This time a wolf ran across the road, but the farmer said: "Drive on, Till; a wolf has crossed our path, and that means good luck for to-day." So they drove into the woods, unharnessed the horse, and left him to eat grass while they chopped down the trees which they thought would be best for building the barn. When they had gotten logs enough, his master sent Till to bring the horse, so that they could load the wagon and drive home. Owlglass started for the place where he had left him. Soon the farmer heard him cry out: "Master, master, come quick! your good luck has come; it has overtaken the horse!"

At this the farmer ran to see what Till meant, and there sat the wolf devouring the poor horse which he had attacked and killed while they were chopping the trees.

"My poor white nag!" wailed the farmer, wringing his hands.

But Till said: "Master, had we driven to the woods the day we saw the hare, *he* would not have eaten the horse; now the wolf has left us nothing but his hide. Let us go home, get your other horse from the stable, harness him to the wagon and drive home with our load of wood."

This they did, and as they drove along, Owlglass sang:

"Early in the morning a soldier vowed he'd slay
  Every Turk who crossed his way.
  Up sprang a little hare,
  Which gave him such a scare,
  That he dared not fight a battle all that day."

Some days after, the farmer told Till to go to town to get a load of bricks for his barn. As he was driving out of the gate, the farmer's wife called after him, and gave him a penny, telling him to bring her a paper of pins.

"Now don't forget," said she, "for I am in a great hurry for them."

As soon as Till reached town he drove to a merchant's, bought a penny's worth of pins, and drove home well pleased with himself. When the farmer saw him coming back with the empty wagon, he asked: "Till, what does this mean? Where are my bricks?"

"They are still at the market," answered Owlglass.

"But the pins I have brought with me," handing the astonished farmer the paper of pins.

"You stupid!" cried the farmer; "would any man send you to town with a horse and wagon just to buy a paper of pins?"

"No man, certainly," replied Till; "but a woman, your wife, told me she was in a hurry for the pins, so I drove back as fast as the horse could go, and this is all the thanks I get."

The farmer lost all patience and dismissed him on the spot, which pleased Owlglass mightily, as by this time he was heartily tired of life on a farm.

TILL AND HIS TRAVELS.

ILL with two travelling companions, a baker and a tailor, journeyed to a neighboring city. On the way they decided whatever they earned or begged they would share in common. The baker and the tailor were great wags, and were always planning to play some kind of a trick upon Owlglass, who appeared to them very honest and simple-minded. It being a warm day, they began to suffer from the heat as they trudged along, so the baker and the tailor gave their coats and bags to Till to carry, and then began to make jokes at his expense. "Brother Till," said the tailor, "we are giving you a great deal of trouble, in fact, burdening you with a donkey's load."

"You are mistaken," replied Owlglass. "It is not a donkey's load, but a load belonging to two donkeys." At this the baker and the tailor said not a word for a long time.

The three comrades now came to a great forest. After wandering about in it for four hours without reaching any house, they decided to camp out under the trees for the night. Upon opening their bags to see how much food they had left for their supper, the baker and the tailor found nothing, and Till only a small quantity of flour. Said the tailor to the baker:

"Bake us a loaf of bread, and we will help you get things ready." So they set to work, the tailor bringing water from a spring near by, the baker kneading the dough, and Owlglass gathering dry sticks for the fire.

While Till was gone in search of more brush wood to feed the flames, the tailor said to the baker : "Let us manage to keep this bread for ourselves, so that we may satisfy our hunger. If we have to share the loaf with Owlglass, there will not be enough for any of us."

"That's true," replied the baker, "but how can we cheat him out of his supper?"

"Leave that to me," answered the tailor, and when Till returned with an armful of wood, he said: "Let us all go to sleep while the bread is baking in the hot ashes, and when we wake up early in the morning, each will tell the others his dream, and he whose dream is the most marvellous shall have the bread." To this his comrades agreed, and all three stretched themselves under the trees and fell asleep. After an hour or two Owlglass woke up so hungry that he could not resist the temptation, but drew the bread out of the ashes and ate it up. Not a crumb did he leave, and without doubt, would have eaten more had there been more to eat. Then he lay down again and slept until morning.

At the first peep of dawn, the tailor and the baker awoke. Said the former joyfully to his comrade: "The bread is ours, for I have had such a wonderful dream. It seemed to me that a bright angel came and led me up to heaven."

"That is a beautiful dream," said the baker, "but

mine was not less wonderful, although it frightened me. It seemed to me that an ugly dwarf came and led me down to hell."

"Ha!" cried the tailor, "the bread is certainly ours. Now let us hear what that simpleton, our friend Till, dreamed about."

Now Owlglass had been awake a long time and had heard all that his comrades had said, although he made believe to be still sleeping. When the baker nudged him and said: "Wake up, brother Till, and tell us your dream," Till yawned and rubbed his eyes, saying:

"What! Have you both come back?"

"Why, you sleepy head, you are dreaming still," said the tailor.

"No, I'm not, I'm awake now," said Owlglass more cheerfully. "I had a very sad dream. It seemed to me that I had lost you both, for one of you was led by a bright angel up to heaven, and the other was led by an ugly dwarf down to hell. As people so seldom come back from either place, I never expected to see you again. So bursting into tears, I raked the bread out of the ashes and ate it up, weeping for you at every mouthful." So spoke Owlglass, and the baker and tailor saw that instead of cheating Till, they had played a joke upon themselves.

Toward evening of the next day, Till and his travelling companions arrived at a large city. Here the baker and the tailor found work, each at his own trade, but Till found nothing to do, for so far his only business in life had been that of playing the fool.

The next morning, as he was strolling through the

town, he saw a sign painter putting fresh paint on a sun dial. Owlglass began talking to the man, and learned from him that the sun dial had to be repainted every year, because the rain washed away the figures on the face.

"No wonder," replied Till; "why don't your town's people build a roof over your sun dial?"

"You are right," said the painter; "I will tell the Mayor."

The Mayor was so pleased with this excellent advice that he sent for Owlglass, thanked him, and gave him two bright silver dollars. He also gave orders to have a roof for the sun dial built at once. But, alas! when the roof was finished the citizens found to their sorrow, that although protected from the rain, the sun dial was now always in shadow.

Till now journeyed on alone to the next town, but reaching it feeling very sad, for he had not only spent his two dollars, but was also suffering from toothache, so that he could scarcely hold up his head. While he was puzzling his mind how to get his tooth pulled, when he had no money to pay the dentist, he happened to pass a bakery, which had a lot of fresh rolls in the show window. He stopped and gazed at the rolls enviously sniffing their appetizing odor. The bake in his white coat stood at the door with his arms folded, looking as contented as people usually do when their work is done. As he was something of a joker, he asked Till how many of those rolls he supposed he could eat.

"I'll bet, over a hundred," said Till.

"Impossible!" cried the baker. "What will you pay me if you lose the bet?"

"I haven't a cent in my pockets," said Till, "but if I do not eat one hundred rolls, I'll pay the bet by having a tooth pulled."

This idea pleased the baker so much that he willingly agreed to the bargain. Owlglass began to eat, and as he was very hungry he succeeded in devouring ten rolls, and then could eat no more. So he said: "I've lost the bet," and let the baker take him to a dentist who pulled the aching tooth. By this means Till was relieved of his hunger and of his pain, but his pockets were still empty. So he cried out in all the streets of the city, that at noon the next day he would fly down from the balcony of the Town Hall, and those who wished to see this great act could do so by coming to the market place and paying one cent each. On the morrow all the people gathered in the market place before the Town Hall, each one bringing a penny. Owlglass took the money, until he had all his pockets full and his cap full too. As the clock in the tower struck twelve, he stepped out upon the balcony and waved his arms as though they were wings. The people stared openmouthed, expecting to see him fly. Then Till laughed and said: "I supposed I was the only fool in the world, but I see here, that in this town there are many greater fools than I. How can I fly when I am neither a goose nor any other kind of bird? I said I *would* fly, and if I had wings I *could*, but without them I cannot."

With these words Till stepped from the balcony, through the window into the Town Hall, and got himself and his money out of the city as speedily as possible.

TILL AND HIS PRANKS.

IN a certain city where the laws were very strict indeed, there lived an innkeeper who was a very proud and conceited man. His favorite boast was that no one could get the best of him. Now it happened that in the course of Till's wanderings he arrived at this very town. He had determined to be on his very best behavior while there, and not indulge in any pranks ; but no sooner did he hear of the innkeeper's boast, than the rogue within him was aroused, and he made up his mind to play a trick upon the boaster. So he went to the tavern, taking with him two cans of the same size. One he concealed under his cloak, and the other he carried openly, and asked the innkeeper to draw him a measure of wine. When his back was turned Till hid the can of wine under his cloak, and produced the other one filled with water, and asked the price of the wine.

" Two cents a measure," said the host.

" That is too dear," said Owlglass ; " I have only sixpence. Take back your wine."

The innkeeper was annoyed at this, but took the can offered him and poured the water into the bunghole of the cask, supposing it to be wine. Till took the can and went away ; but just as he was going out of the door, he turned and said : " I see that you are a fool, for even a fool can hoodwink you."

These words naturally vexed the wine merchant, and
the longer he thought of them the more he made up
his mind that Owlglass had played some trick on him.
So he ran for the market inspector, and went with him
in pursuit of Till, whom they soon overtook. When
they found him carrying two cans instead of one, they
arrested him as a thief and put him in jail. Till feared
the worst, for in those days thieves were often hanged;
so on the day of his trial he pleaded thus: "O wise
and honorable citizens, I am no thief, but only a fool,
and like all fools, I sometimes speak the truth. The
innkeeper's brag led me on to take the wine, not in
order to steal it, but to show him that even a fool
could get the best of him." This influenced the people,
for many of them bore a grudge against the innkeeper,
and rejoiced that his pride had had a fall, so Till was
allowed to go free. The citizens felt that it would
never do for future generations to say of them that
they hanged a man simply for being a fool. Owlglass
had come so near an untimely end that he lost no
time in shaking the dust of that town from his feet.
He continued his pilgrimage until he reached a little
village on the bank of a river. Here he found great
excitement, for the villagers had set apart that day for
a fishing expedition.

The previous summer their mayor had brought from
a neighboring town a score of herrings. These tasted
so good to him, that he called the villagers together
and proposed to them the advisability of breeding
herrings in their mill-pond, to which they agreed. So
a ton of salt herrings was brought to the village and
put into the mill-pond. Since then a year had passed

and the villagers had hoped to find that the herrings had multiplied so that they would get a larger draught of fishes.

When Till arrived, he was invited to take part in the festivities. A fish net was dragged through the pond, and all eyes were fastened to the spot where it was to be drawn out of the water. But imagine the disappointment when no herrings came to the surface, only a great fat eel wriggling in the meshes of the net. After a moment of surprise, the villagers grew angry and cried : " The wicked eel has gobbled up all our herrings." It was plain that such greediness deserved a severe penalty.

" He must die ! " cried the mayor.

All agreed to this, but were undecided as to what death would best befit this crime.

" Let us hang him," said one.

" Fry him," cried another.

" Far too easy a death," said Owlglass. " Why not drown him ? "

All were delighted with this idea, so the eel was carried to the river, and thrown with great force upon its muddy bank. The eel no sooner felt the wet ground under him than he crawled about and soon reached the water, and wriggled about with delight in his native element. The villagers took his squirming to be his death agony, and came away perfectly satisfied with the punishment they had inflicted. They thanked Till for his good advice, and urged him to prolong his stay with them, but Owlglass resumed his wanderings, saying to himself : " There are too many fools here now."

He travelled on until he reached the North Sea. **As**

he walked along the shore one pleasant day, he saw a party of men in bathing. Suddenly one of them cried: "Wait, friends, and let me count to see if we are all here. One of our number seems to be missing." So he began and counted eight, but forgot to count himself. At this he was overcome with fright and said: "We were nine, *one* must be drowned!"

"Let me count," said another; but he forgot to count himself just as the first one had done. The swimmers now felt sure that one of their number must be drowned, and they swam sorrowfully to the shore. As they stood bewailing their loss, Till asked them what the trouble was.

"Oh! sir!" they cried, "we were nine, and now we are only eight. One of us must be drowned, but we cannot tell which."

"I can readily solve the riddle," said Owlglass. "Lie down every one of you and stick your noses into the sand." This they did.

"Now stand up," continued he.

They rose as one man.

"Now count the dents in the sand. So many dents, so many noses, so many men."

They counted and gave a shout of joy.

"Hurrah!" cried they, "nine dents, nine noses, nine men. There is no one drowned!"

Thanking Till for his help, they went joyfully home, and Owlglass resumed his pilgrimage.

The next person he met was a barber, who asked him to what trade he belonged.

"I am a barber," replied Owlglass, who had readily guessed his questioner's occupation. The barber hired him at once, being in need of help, and pointed out his shop saying : " See that house with the large windows ? go in there, and I shall soon follow you."

Till went directly to the house, and walked right through the window, smashing the glass into bits.

" Good-day," said he to the barber's wife, who sat quietly sewing.

The woman jumped from her chair in a fright, saying : " Who are you, breaking into my house in this way ? Was not the door wide enough ? "

" Do not be angry, madam," said Owlglass, " your husband has just hired me, and I am obeying his orders."

By this time the barber had arrived ; and when he saw what damage Till had done, instead of scolding him, he thought to himself, " I'll keep him, and take the price of the broken glass out of his wages." So he had the window panes reset without delay. After Owlglass had worked for him for several days, he bade him sharpen his shears. This Till did, grinding the back of his scissors as fine and sharp as the front. When the barber discovered the mischief Till had been guilty of he lost his temper and cried : " You are an arch rogue ! Leave me and go whence you came."

" Very well! " said Owlglass, and jumped through the very window by which he had entered the shop a few days before. The barber ran after the jailer, and together they pursued Till, hoping to catch him and make him pay for the broken glass. But Owlglass was fleeter than barber or bailiff. He reached the seashore, jumped on a boat that was homeward bound, and sailed away.

TILL A LANDOWNER.

IT was now several years since Owlglass had bade his mother good-bye, and he longed to see her again. So he returned to the little village where he had done his rope dancing in former years, and where she still lived. This time his friends and relatives received their rich cousin Till so much more cordially than they had on his earlier visit when he had come back poor, that he felt vexed with them, and urged his mother to leave the town, and go with him to the neighboring village which was his birthplace. To this she agreed, so Owlglass bought a little house and a few acres of land and settled down in the home of his childhood.

Till's providing a home for his mother in her old age made her very happy. She was very proud of him, and so pleased with his courteous manners and knowledge of the world, that she asked him where he had learned so much politeness.

"Among the rudest and gruffest people, dear mother," said Owlglass, "for I always noticed what displeased me in their behavior, in order to avoid the same faults in my own conduct."

The villagers had great respect for Till's wisdom, and asked his advice in all matters of importance.

Even the Mayor consulted him one day, and asked his opinion in regard to a very puzzling case, which was as follows:

Two brothers who had inherited five hundred dollars from their father, asked their aunt to take charge of the money and keep it for them, until they should return from their travels. The agreement was that she should give the entire sum to both, and not part of it to either one. The brothers departed, and nothing was heard of them for a long time, until finally one of them returned and said: "Dear aunt, my poor brother died in a foreign land; give me the inheritance which we entrusted to your care." The old woman, without any suspicion of wrong doing, gave her nephew the five hundred dollars, with which he soon left the village. After six months the elder brother returned, and made the same request, saying his brother was dead.

The aunt turned pale with fright, and told him that his brother had led her to believe that he was dead, and that she had given the money to him. He insisted upon having his inheritance, and brought his aunt to the mayor, who could suggest no way out of the difficulty except for the poor old woman to sell her house and land in order to pay him what he demanded, but before giving his decision he came to Till for his advice in the matter.

Owlglass appeared in court on the day of the trial, and asked the aunt whether it had been arranged that she was to keep the money until both brothers came and asked for it together. To this she said, " Yes."

"Then," said Till to the nephew, "produce your brother, and when you appear together, you shall receive your inheritance."

" But, sir, my brother is dead," said he.

" In that case you can never obtain the money, for the agreement was that you should receive it together," said Owlglass.

This frightened the fellow so, that he became confused, made all sorts of excuses to obtain the money, and finally contradicted himself, so that Till discovered that his brother was still living, and that this plot had been hatched between them in order to get double the money from the aunt. Upon this the deceiver was put in jail to await the return of his brother.

Till received so much praise for his judgment in this and other matters that his fame spread to a neighboring town, the very place where he had advised the inhabitants to bury their town bell in the lake, and which they had never been able to recover. Now that Owlglass lived so near, it occurred to the mayor of the town to ask him to make good their loss.

" What need have you of a bell?" Till asked the mayor.

" Principally for the purpose of ringing it whenever we see a storm coming," he replied.

" I know a better way to foretell the weather than by ringing a bell," said Owlglass. " While I was in Rome I learned how to control the weather, and will do it for you for a year if you will let me know just what kind you want."

The mayor was a cautious man, and before he agreed to withdraw his request for a bell, he asked Owlglass to prove his power over the weather by making the next day a pleasant one. Till promised to do so, and on the morrow the sun shone brightly from morning till evening. This convinced the mayor, so he came the next day with such great faith in Till's ability, that he asked him to arrange the weather for a year, the mayor writing to him from month to month, and telling him just what kind he wanted.

"But what you desire might not suit the rest of your townspeople," said Owlglass. "Go home and consult them, and when you have all agreed upon the weather let me know."

"You are right," said the mayor, and went home and called a meeting of all the villagers. But, although the meeting lasted over a month, they could come to no agreement, as each one wanted weather to suit his own particular plans. So finally, after a very stormy meeting, they sent word to Till that they could not decide upon the weather, and begged him to give them the bell instead. Although he could not very well afford it, Owlglass now felt obliged to make the villagers a present of a bell; but as they had said nothing about a tongue for it, he sent them a bell without one. The villagers wondered and wondered why their new bell made no sound when rung, and never discovered the difficulty until a year after, when a bell manufacturer passed through their village and solved the mystery. Upon this they had a tongue made for the bell at their own expense, and were so delighted with the result, that they rang their bell so loud and often that it could be heard even as far as the village in which Till lived.

After a few years of this peaceful life, Owlglass' mother died, and the longing for travel was aroused once more in his heart. So Till sold his little home, saddled his horse, and rode forth into the world again.

One day, while stopping at a tavern on the banks of the Rhine the cook was so late in putting the meat over the fire that dinner was delayed beyond the noon hour, and Owlglass became vexed. The landlord noticed his indignation, and said: "He who cannot wait for a meal, must eat what he can." Till drew a roll from his pocket, and seated himself before the hearth in the kitchen, and while he turned and basted the roast from time to time, he held the roll over the meat, so that the steam from cooking saturated the soft bread, and then he ate it.

Long after twelve o'clock, the dinner was served, and the host and his guests seated themselves at the table. But Owlglass remained in the kitchen by the fire. When the landlady asked him if he did not want anything to eat he said: "No, the steam from the cooking has taken away my appetite."

Afterward when the others had finished and paid for their dinner, the host came into the kitchen and asked Till to pay him twenty-five cents.

"Is it your custom to demand payment from guests who have eaten nothing of your providing? You gave me nothing, why should I pay?" asked Owlglass.

"You satisfied your hunger with the steam from my roast," answered the innkeeper, "and that is as good as a meal, for which, Master Till, you must pay!"

Owlglass drew a piece of silver from his purse, threw it upon the table and said: "Do you hear it ring, mine host?"

"Certainly, I hear it," replied the landlord.

"Very well," said Till, putting the money back into his pocket, "may the ring of the metal do you as much good as the steam from the roast did me. Let the one pay for the other."

The angry innkeeper did not dare summon Owlglass before the court of justice, fearing he would play another prank upon him.

It happened to be a time of political discord in the land, over the rival claims of the old king and the new. So Owlglass proceeded at once to the young king's camp near Frankfort, hoping to find employment there. On the way he was soon overtaken by the Archbishop and his retinue. The Archbishop, who was an affable man, noticed Till's peculiar costume, and asked him whether he were not too thinly clad, adding: "It is a chilly day and I feel cold."—"Is it a cold day?" asked Owlglass. "I do not feel cold; if your reverence will give me a dollar, I will tell you how to keep warm." The Archbishop gave him the dollar, and Till said: "Every man feels the cold according to his clothing. I have on all the clothes I possess, consequently I keep warm. If your reverence would put on all your clothing, you would no longer feel the cold."

The Archbishop laughed and said: "If I wore all my clothes at once, no horse could carry me. Nevertheless you have earned your dollar, even if I cannot follow your advice. Tell me, what is your trade?" continued the Archbishop after a short pause.

"I am a spectacle maker," said Till, "and give people glasses through which to study the world, but lately there has been little demand for my spectacles, for those in authority look at the world through their fingers. They spend their time trying to win grace and favor rather than trying to study the difference between right

and wrong in order to deal justly by everyone. Neither
do the priests spend their time reading and praying as
they used to, and the evil has spread so far that even
the magistrates and justices look through their fingers
instead of my spectacles." The Archbishop was so
pleased with Till's little sermon that he invited him
to come and live at his court.

Upon the arrival of the Archbishop at Frankfort, a
merchant who had just come from another town, complained to him that just before entering Frankfort, he
had lost a saddle-bag containing eight hundred dollars.
The Archbishop had it announced in all the churches
that the finder of the bag should receive a reward of one
hundred dollars upon restoring the money to the merchant. Soon after this a poor carpenter came to the
Archbishop's court, bringing the saddle-bag and the eight
hundred dollars. The merchant was so pleased to recover his property, that he threw five dollars to the
carpenter, saying he need not give him the hundred
dollars, as he had probably helped himself to that
already, as there were nine hundred dollars in the bag
when he lost it, and now there were only eight hundred.
The carpenter indignantly spurned the five dollars with
his foot, declaring that he was an honorable man, and
had taken neither one dollar nor one hundred out of
the bag. The Archbishop brought the case to trial, but
as the merchant swore that he had lost nine hundred
dollars, and the carpenter swore that he had only found
eight hundred, he could not decide what to do, until
Owlglass came to the rescue, saying that, as the merchant had lost nine hundred dollars, and the carpenter
had found only eight hundred, the bag could not pos-

sibly belong to the merchant, and that the carpenter must keep it until the rightful owner came to claim his property. The Archbishop and all his court were greatly pleased with Till's shrewd solution of the difficulty.

TILL AND THE ARCHBISHOP.

WLGLASS indulged in many pranks while at court, much to the amusement of the Archbishop, who often laughed heartily at his capers. Till became very fond of the Archbishop, and frequently when he noticed that the cares of the government pressed heavily upon him, Owlglass would endeavor with his nonsense to make his master smile, and thus drive the clouds from his brow. Early one morning the Archbishop stood at a window of the palace facing the market place. He looked unusually worried, so Till took his stand beneath the window with a large wooden tub in front of him. As the farmers' wives came to market with milk to sell, he bought of each one, all she had, and let her pour it into his tub, marking the number of quarts with a piece of chalk on the outside. The women stood about, waiting for their pay, which Owlglass promised them as soon as his tub should be full. When it was filled to the brim, he said: "I have no money to-day, but will pay you all in two weeks if you can wait that long. If you cannot, take back your milk."

The women first looked puzzled, then angry. Then each tried to dip out the milk she had poured into the tub. This soon led to a quarrel. They pulled and pushed, and finally struck at each other with their pails, until all the milk was spilled and thrown about the place. The men, attempting to separate the women, mixed in the strife, until the whole market was in an uproar. The battle lasted as long as there was a drop of milk left in the tub, much to the amusement of the spectators. The Archbishop at his window laughed until he had to hold his sides. When he learned that Till had perpetrated this prank for his entertainment, he sent his servant down to pay the women for their milk, and to thank Owlglass for the amusement he had furnished him.

The market inspector, however, was not so well pleased with the disturbance, and complained to the mayor, who at once sent for Till. The latter dressed himself in rags, and presented himself at the mayor's house. The servant who answered his knock, told him, without asking who he was, that his master was busy, and could not see him. So Owlglass, satisfied that he had done what was required of him, went away. A week after, the mayor sent for him again. This time Till dressed himself in the Archbishop's livery of red velvet and silver, and went again to the mayor's house. This time he was admitted at once, and ushered into the mayor's presence. Without saying a word, Owlglass began to kiss his red velvet coat, and the Archbishop's crest embroidered on it.

"What does this mean?" asked the mayor in surprise. "Why do you kiss your coat?"

"Not my coat, but the Archbishop's," answered Till. "I do it because this coat admitted me to your presence. I was here eight days ago, in my own ragged coat, but you were busy and could not see me; but to-day, I am admitted at once, on account of the Archbishop's livery." The mayor saw that he had been at fault, and so tried to make amends by reprimanding Owlglass as leniently as possible for the disturbance he had created at the market, telling him in future not to set the market women to quarrelling.

" I will remember," said Till.

Owlglass refrained for so long a time after this from joking, that the Archbishop noticed it, and asked him why he was so changed.

" I am learning the Black Art," said Till.

The Archbishop laughed, and asked Owlglass to give him a proof of his powers as a magician.

" Come with me to the market," said Till, " and I will show you a woman who has earthen-ware for sale. Without speaking to her, I will cast a spell over her by my incantations, so that she will get up, seize a stick, and break every one of her dishes in pieces."

The Archbishop was so incredulous, that he offered a wager of thirty dollars that Owlglass could not do it. So they went together to the market, and Till showed his master from a distance which woman he would bewitch. Then he began to mutter to himself, and make strange gestures as though casting a spell over his victim. Suddenly the woman sprang to her feet, seized a stick, and beat her crockery as though possessed, until every dish was broken into a thousand pieces. The Archbishop stared in astonishment, and as soon as they had returned to the palace he took Owlglass to his room, locked and bolted the door, and after paying him the wager, promised to give him a fat ox if he would divulge the secret of his witchcraft.

"My Black Art," said Till, "consisted in paying the
woman beforehand the price of her wares, and telling
her to smash everything at a given signal from me."

TILL AS COURT JESTER.

AT the approach of winter the Archbishop
died, and Owlglass realized that he must
soon resume his wanderer's life once more.
For by the time the court laid aside its
garb of mourning, another prince was at
the helm of the Church ship. His new master took no
pleasure in Till's nonsense, and consequently he was
no longer happy there. He left the court, however,
with a purse so well filled that he could have travelled
a year and a day without coming to want. He rode
gaily through Saxony, his native land, until he reached
Poland. Here he noticed that all officers, magistrates,
secretaries and others in the king's service received
much consideration, and became rich by oppressing the
people, but that the peasants remained poor under this
form of government. Till's rustic blood took umbrage
at this injustice, and he immediately bethought himself
of a plan to remedy the evil. He went to the king and
begged him to give him a government position, a little
one, no matter how small, so that he, too, could become
rich, like all others in his service. The king answered
gruffly that government offices were not for the benefit
of the few, but for the good of all.

"Your Majesty," replied Owlglass, "let me be the
herdsman of your cattle for several years. I will serve
entirely without pay."

The king was satisfied with this offer, and Till entered into his service as herdsman to the royal cattle. He realized that even in this humble capacity, he was not without influence, so he wrote to each city in Poland, saying that he had learned that there was good pasturage in that neighborhood, and that he would bring the royal cattle there to graze. This, naturally, alarmed the citizens of the various towns, for they feared that the king's sheep and cows would leave but scant pasturage for their own flocks and herds; so they, one and all, sent Owl-glass large sums of money, begging him not to come. By this means he soon received more money than he could spend.

One day as he was pasturing his flocks and herds near a dense forest, he noticed from the uneasiness of the sheep and cattle, that a beast of prey must be in the neighborhood. He went into the forest to look, and soon discovered a great bear leading her cub. On coming nearer, Till saw that the little bear was blind, and followed after its mother by keeping hold of her tail with its mouth. Owlglass watched his opportunity, and cut the big bear's tail off with his sword, leaving the end of it still in the little bear's mouth. Till took hold of the tail and led the cub in this way for two miles, until he reached the palace. The king and all the royal family shook with laughter when they saw the strange pair enter the courtyard, and hurried down-stairs to get a nearer view.

Owlglass made the king a present of his little pris-oner. His majesty was so delighted with the gift, that he asked Till whether he would reward him with a

handful of gold pieces, a horse, some sheep, or several
acres of land.

"Your majesty," replied Till, "with your gracious permission, I shall put the gold pieces in my pocket, mount
the horse, drive the sheep before me, look with grate-
ful eyes upon the land, and pray for the long life of my
king."

This answer pleased the king so well, that he gave
Owlglass all that he asked for instead of only giving
him the choice of one gift.

So, richly rewarded, Owlglass returned to his flocks
and herds. The money which he received as bribes
from the different cities from time to time made him
so rich that he dressed like a prince, and wore a choice
fox skin and peacock's feathers in his cap. One day
when the king was out riding, he met Till arrayed in
all his splendor, and asked him how it was possible for
his herdsman to be so well dressed when he received no
pay.

"Your majesty," said Owlglass, "it is not by means
of wages that I have gained wealth, but because I
manage just as the other royal servants do." And then
he told the king frankly what he had done, and how he
had extracted bribes from the people by virtue of his
position in the king's service.

"By my faith," cried the king, "I had not thought
of the matter in that light. This shall be changed!"
So saying, he graciously extended his hand to Till,
assured him of his royal favor and invited him to come
and live with him at the palace as court jester, saying:
"Be ever at my side, and when you are moved to do so,
tell me the plain unvarnished truth!"

Till accepted the offer, and lived from that time on at court. One day the king and his household went hunting, so that there was no one left at home except two cooks, the court tailor, the poet laureate, a butcher and Till Owlglass, his pet dog and the bear. The hunting party was scarcely out of sight, when these servants ran out to visit and gossip with the neighbors, so there was no one left in the palace except Owlglass, his dog and the young bear. For pastime, Till unchained the bear and amused himself with his antics. In romping about the great hall, Bruin happened to strike against a window and break it. The noise of the broken glass pleased the bear so well, that he struck his paw against all the other windows, and broke one after another.

In the meantime the two cooks, the tailor, the poet and the butcher came home and saw what damage had been done. As there was no way of concealing it, they determined to tell the king what had happened as soon as he returned. So when the king and his followers rode into the courtyard toward evening, the two cooks, the tailor, the poet and the butcher threw themselves at his majesty's feet, and begging for mercy, told him about the broken windows and the bear. The king immediately asked who had unchained the bear, adding that the guilty one should have both ears cut off for punishment.

Each one declared his innocence except Owlglass, who remained silent for a moment, then turned to his dog, who stood beside him, and whispered audibly: "Do not betray your master, or I shall lose my ears." Every one heard this and laughed, especially the king, who forgave Till for the mischief he and the bear had caused.

Thinking that his ears were in more or less danger after this incident, Owlglass had a pair of long ears made out of cloth and sewed to his cap; saying that the king could cut off these whenever he felt the need of a pair of fool's ears. Upon this, the king presented Till with a gaily colored leather sceptre, at the end of which was a head adorned with a fool's cap and bells, and said as he handed it to him : "This mock sceptre represents your badge of office at my court. Use it well and give it to no one, unless you find a greater fool than yourself."

Not long after this, the king became very ill. The doctor came every day, and would say to the queen and courtiers, shaking his head : "The king is going on a long journey."

Each time Owlglass heard these words, he went to the stable, hid himself in a corner and wept, for he loved the king very much indeed. But one day after a fit of weeping, Owlglass dried his tears, forced himself to look cheerful, and went to the sick room. He approached the king's bedside and told him he had just been to the stable to see if arrangements were being made for the journey, but nothing was ready.

"What journey?" asked the king.

"Yours, my lord and king," said Till. "They tell me you are going on a long journey, but I see you are making no preparations for it. So I have come to give back the sceptre which you lent me; for if I were going on a long journey, I should be getting ready, so I have come to the conclusion that you are a greater

fool than I. Take the sceptre. It belongs by right to
you."

At this the king was forced to laugh in spite of his
sufferings. From that moment he began to mend, and
was soon restored to health, and lived to rule his king-
dom for many years.

TILL AND THE POET.

NE day the king stood at a window of the
palace and gazed with pride upon his soldiers, assembled before the castle. They
were all armed and equipped for battle.
Owlglass stepped up to the king and asked where they
were going.

"They are going to war," replied the king.

"And what will they do there?" asked Owlglass.

"They will destroy fields and orchards, burn and plun-
der villages, pursue and kill the enemy," said the king.

"For what purpose?" continued Till.

"So that peace may be restored, you fool!" replied
the king.

"Would it not be better to arrange for peace before
the battle and avoid all this devastation and blood-
shed?" asked Till.

"You are right!" cried the king, and at once sent
messengers to arrange a treaty of peace. So Owlglass
was the means of saving many lives, and instead of having a war, the king gave a festival in honor of peace.

At this celebration there were to be artistic fireworks
in the gardens of the palace, which were to be set off in
the evening. After the court gardener had everything
in readiness, he told Till he feared the fireworks might

not be a success, so the latter suggested his touching a match to the different pieces to see if they were all right. The gardener thinking this a good idea applied the match, and so the fireworks were let off in broad daylight, with no one to enjoy the spectacle but Owlglass and himself. When the king and his household assembled in the evening, to see the grand display, there were no fireworks to be seen. They had to content themselves with Till's description of their magnificence.

Another feature of the Peace Festival programme was a poem written by the poet-laureate in honor of the occasion. The poet was a little man, but great in his own esteem. He tried to make himself look tall by wearing his hair in long waves, and wrapping himself up in a long cloak. He recited his poem to the lords and ladies of the court in a tragic voice, and waved his arms, and stamped his feet so violently, that some of the courtiers could not keep from smiling, and the maids of honor giggled aloud. At this the poet-laureate flew into a rage, and abused his audience, in such loud tones, that the king heard the disturbance, and came into the hall, and asked what all the noise was about. Till gave an amusing account of the scene, imitating the little poet so perfectly in voice and manner, that the king and all his court were convulsed with laughter. At this outburst of ridicule the crestfallen versifier slunk away without a word, but meditating revenge in his heart against Owlglass. That same evening a play was given in honor of the Peace Festival, and during the performance, Owlglass, who was a big fellow, managed to stand in front of the little poet and obscure his view of the stage. No matter how the little man turned about or stretched his neck, the burly Saxon stood before him. The poet, who was still nursing his wrath from their last encounter, grew still angrier, and tried to shove Owlglass one side, but to no purpose. Finally he tugged at Till's sleeve, and told him that he prevented his seeing anything of the play.

Owlglass said : " Master Poet, you have always looked at me without seeing me, why don't you do so now ? "

This made the little verse-maker so furious that he called Owlglass a churl, and challenged him to fight a duel.

Till accepted the challenge, and the next morning at the appointed hour, arrived with a large party of friends at a meadow, on the outskirts of the town, the place agreed upon for the duel. Here, looking pale and nervous in the early morning light, he found the poet with his second awaiting him. Each opponent was given a sword and shown where to stand. Just as the rays of sunlight gilded the neighboring tree tops, the signal was given for the combat to commence.

Owlglass plunged his sword into the grass in front of him, seized his riding whip and defended himself from his enemy's sword thrusts with that. He handled the whip so cleverly, that he very soon swung it around the blade of his opponent's sword, jerked the weapon out of his hand, and swung it high into the air. Then leaning both hands upon the hilt of his sword, still sticking in the grass, Till said to the dazed poet: " Well, my little man, is your honor satisfied ? " Then without waiting for a reply, he turned, swung himself into his saddle and rode away smiling.

TILL IN DISGRACE.

O N Sunday morning when the king and his court were at church Owlglass felt so hungry that he went down to the royal kitchen to see if he could not get something to eat. The cook was busy roasting a crane and some pheasants, the odor of which was most appetizing. Till begged for a morsel fresh from the pan.

"I dare not give you any," said the cook. "I should lose my place if I did, for no one may dine before the king."

At this Owlglass took a knife and cut a leg from the crane, helped himself to bread and wine, and ate and drank until his hunger was satisfied. When the mutilated crane was placed before the king at dinner, he asked at once: "Where is the other leg?"

None of the servants dared reply, and the king would have been angry had not Till, who stood behind his chair, whispered in his ear: "Do not be vexed, Your Majesty, I will show you after dinner that all cranes have but one leg."

The king did not seem satisfied with this reply, so Owlglass hastened to divert his attention by asking a guest who sat at table wearing magnificent jewels, how much one of his precious stones cost.

"Three hundred dollars," the nobleman replied.

"And this one?" asked Till, pointing to another.

" Six hundred dollars."

" What income do they bring you?" continued Owlglass.

" None, you fool; they cost money, but they do not bring in any," said the nobleman.

" Then I can show you far more valuable stones," said Till, " two of which furnish their owner with an income of six hundred dollars a year."

The nobleman was incredulous, and asked to see them. So after dinner, Owlglass led the entire court to a mill pond, and showed them two mill stones, which he explained brought the miller an income of six hundred dollars a year.

Then said the king: " Now prove to me that a crane has only one leg."

Till next conducted the royal household to a field where there were about thirty or forty cranes, each standing upon one leg.

" See, Your Majesty," said Owlglass, " each bird has only one leg."

The king clapped his hands, so that the cranes were startled and flew away, each one stretching two legs behind him.

" Now, Till," said he, " you see that each crane has two legs."

" If Your Majesty had clapped your hands at dinner, the crane would have stretched out his other leg, too, and flown away," replied Owlglass.

Till had now lived several years at the Polish Court, and although he liked it, the desire for travel seized him again, and he longed for a wandering life once more, but had no good excuse for leaving his royal

master. The king had a horse of which he was so
fond, that he often said, that when the horse died, he
would be so unhappy that whoever brought him the
news of his favorite's death should be hanged. At last
the horse did die, and no one dared tell the king.
Finally Owlglass summoned up courage and rushed into
the king's presence. Bursting into tears, he cried out:
"Your Majesty, your horse! Your poor horse! Only
yesterday it was —"

"The king hastily interrupted him, saying: "Is my
horse dead? I feel sure that he is; yes, he must be
dead!"

"Alas, my lord and king! that is not the worst of it,"
cried Till.

"Well! what else?" asked the king.

"Ah! to think that you must be hanged! for you
were the first to say that the horse was dead," replied
Owlglass.

The king was very much distressed over the death of
his favorite, but could not help laughing at Till's sauci-
ness in breaking the unwelcome news.

Just at this time the king had occasion to send an
embassy to the King of Denmark, so he decided to send
Owlglass with the ambassadors, telling him that his way
of sugaring a pill would cause his message to be well
received at the Danish Court.

TILL'S LAST JOURNEY.

WLGLASS and the ambassadors sailed across the sea, and found upon arriving at the Danish Court, that Till's fame as a joker had preceded him; for in every land Owlglass and his pranks were talked about, and many an emperor and king would have given a great deal to secure Till as a jester for his own court. The King of Denmark considered it a proof of his royal cousin of Poland's most distinguished consideration, that Owlglass was sent to him and allowed to remain even for a short time. No sooner had Till appeared at the Danish Court, than the king, who loved nothing better than a joke, asked Owlglass to play some prank for his amusement. Till promised to do so, and asked whether the king would allow him to have his horse shod. The king gave his consent, telling Owlglass to have him shod with the very best shoes, at his expense. So Till rode to a goldsmith, and had his horse shod with gold shoes and silver nails. When the goldsmith presented his bill the king was indignant at the price, and asked Owlglass what he meant by ordering such expensive horse shoes.

"Because you commanded me, your majesty," said he, "to get the very best, and I thought there was nothing better than gold and silver, and obeyed your commands."

The king laughed and said: "I see you are a faithful servant, who does as he is told." He paid the bill, but did not ask Till to play any more pranks.

After the ambassadors had delivered their message they returned to Poland, but Owlglass did not embark with them for the homeward voyage. He preferred to make the journey by land, for he did not love the sea. So after having the golden horse shoes removed and replaced by iron ones, he mounted his cream-colored steed, and turned his steps toward Poland. He had not proceeded very far beyond the borders of Germany, however, when he became very ill, and was taken to a hospital. Here, while being cared for by the nuns, he was visited by many people, friends and acquaintances, who came to inquire after his health. Even the mayor of the town came and asked him whether he had any wish that he would like fulfilled.

" Yes, I have one wish," said Till turning his face to those standing about his bed. " Will you grant it?"

All promised to fulfil his wish and Owlglass said : " I thank you, I have only one wish, and that is that you all go to your homes and leave me to die in peace."

Till grew rapidly worse, and he felt that his end was near. So he made his will, dividing his property into three parts; one-third he left to his friends, one-third to the mayor of the town, and one-third to the priest, with the request that the locked and beautifully ornamented chest which contained his treasures should not be opened until four weeks after his death. This box his heirs received with thanks, and promised to carry out his wishes, sharing amicably whatever they should find in the chest.

A few days after this Owlglass died, and was laid in

his coffin. At the churchyard, as his body was about
to be lowered into the grave, the rope at the foot of
the coffin broke, and the casket slid into the grave in
such a position that Till's body was upright, as though
he was standing upon his feet.

"Let him remain so," said the mourners; "he was so
peculiar in life, let him be peculiar even in death."

So the coffin was left as it was, the grave was filled,
and a head-stone placed above it, upon which was
carved an owl holding a mirror in its claw, and below
these lines:

> "Touch not this stone with ruthless hands,
> For buried here Till Owlglass stands.
> Anno Domini, MCCCL."

Four weeks after Till's death, the mayor, the priest
and Till's friends came together to open the chest, in
order to divide their inheritance. When they turned
the key in the lock and raised the cover, they found
nothing inside but paving stones. The heirs looked at
each other at first, speechless with astonishment, then
after a moment, they began to accuse each other of
having made away with the treasure, and so they
parted in anger and strife. For none of them knew
that Owlglass had left his possessions behind him in
Poland, whither he expected to return. This last prank
showed his ruling passion strong in death, and was as
characteristic of his odd genius as the way in which he
was buried.

> With this prank ends the story,
> Of a joker in word and deed.
> Those whom his nonsense pleases,
> The book again may read.

AMONG THE LIONS OF ALGIERS

(FROM TARTARIN OF TARASCON.)

BY ALPHONSE DAUDET.

O N the 1st of December, 18—, in
clear, brilliant, splendid weather,
under a south winter sun, the
startled inhabitants of Marseilles
beheld a Turk come down Canebière
Street. A Turk, a regular Turk —
never had such a one been seen; and
yet, Heaven knows, there is no lack
of Turks at Marseilles.

The Turk in question — do I need
tell you it was the great Tartarin of Tarascon? —
waddled along the quays, followed by his gun-cases,
medicine-chest, and tinned comestibles, to reach the
landing-stage of the Touache Company and the mail
steamer the Zouave, which was to transport him over
the sea.

With his ears still ringing with the home applause,
intoxicated by the glare of the heavens and the reek of
the sea, Tartarin fairly beamed as he stepped out with
a lofty head, and between his guns on his shoulders,
looking with all his eyes upon that wondrous, dazzling
harbor of Marseilles, which he saw for the first time.

The poor fellow believed he was dreaming. He fancied his name was Sindbad the Sailor, and that he was roaming in one of those fantastic cities abundant in the "Arabian Nights." As far as eye could reach there

spread a forest of masts and spars, cris-crossing in every way.

Flags of all countries floated—English, American, Russian, Swedish, Greek, and Tunisian.

The vessels lay alongside the wharves—ay, head on, so that their bowsprits stuck up out over the strand like rows of bayonets. Over it, too, sprawled the

"THE TURK IN QUESTION."

mermaids, goddesses, madonnas, and other figure-heads in carved and painted wood which gave names to the ships—all worn by sea-water, split, mildewed, and dripping. Ever and anon, between the hulls, lay a patch of harbor like watered silk splashed with oil. In the intervals of the yards and booms, what seemed swarms of flies prettily spotted the blue sky. These were the sailor-boys, hailing one another in all languages. . . .

All the time a frightful riot, the rumbling of carts, the "Haul all, haul away!" of the sailors, oaths, songs, steamboat whistles, the bugles and drums in Forts Saint Jean and Saint Nicolas, the bells of the Major, the Accoules, and Saint Victor; with the mistral atop of all, catching up the noises and clamor, and rolling them up together with a furious shaking, till confounded with its own voice, which intoned a mad, wild, heroic melody like a grand charging tune — one that filled hearers with a longing to be off, and the farther the better — a craving for wings.

To the sound of this splendid blast the intrepid Tartarin of Tarascon embarked for the land of lions. . . .

On board the Zouave the company was as jolly as numerous, composed of officers going back to join their regiments, ladies from the Marseilles Alcazar Music Hall, strolling-players, a rich Mussulman returning from Mecca, and a very jocular Montenegrin prince, who favored them with imitations of the low comedians of Paris. Not one of these jokers felt the sea-sickness, and their time was passed in quaffing champagne with the steamer captain, a good fat born Marseillais, who had a wife and family as well at Algiers as at home, and who answered to the merry name of Barbassou.

Tartarin of Tarascon hated this pack of wretches; their mirthfulness deepened his ails.

At length, on the third afternoon, there was such an extraordinary hullabaloo on the deck that our hero was roused out of his long torpor. The ship's bell was ringing and the seamen's heavy boots ran over the planks.

" Go ahead! Stop her! Back her!" barked the hoarse voice of Captain Barbassou; and then, "Stop her dead!"

There was an abrupt cessation of movement, a shock, and no more, save the silent rolling of the boat from side to side like a balloon in the air. This strange stillness alarmed the Tarasconian.

" Heaven ha' mercy upon us ! " he yelled in a terrifying voice, as, recovering his strength by magic, he
bounded out of his berth, and rushed upon deck with
his arsenal.

Only the arrival, not a foundering.

The Zouave was just gliding into the roadstead — a
fine one of black, deep water, but dull and still, almost

deserted. On elevated ground
ahead rose Algiers, the White City,
with its little houses of a dead
cream-color huddling against one
another lest they should slide into
the sea. It was like Meudon slope
with a laundress's washing hung
out to dry. Over it a vast blue
satin sky — and such a blue !

A little restored from his fright,
the illustrious Tartarin gazed
on the landscape, and listened
with respect to the Montenegrin prince, who stood by
his side as he named the different parts of the capital,
the Kasbah, the upper town,
and the Rue Bab-Azoon. A
very finely-brought-up prince
was this Montenegrin; moreover, knowing Algeria thoroughly, and speaking Arabic

"To Arms ! To Arms !"

fluently. Hence Tartarin thought of cultivating his
acquaintance.

All at once, along the bulwark against which they

were leaning, the Tarasconian perceived a row of large black hands clinging to it from over the side. Almost instantly a negro's woolly head shot up before him, and, ere he had time to open his mouth, the deck was overwhelmed on every side by a hundred black or yellow desperadoes, half naked, hideous and fearsome. Tartarin knew who these pirates were — " they," of course, the celebrated " they" who had too often been hunted after by him in the by-ways of Tarascon. At last they had decided to meet him face to face. At the outset surprise nailed him to the spot. But when he saw the outlaws fall upon the luggage, tear off the tarpaulin covering, and actually commence the pillage of the ship, then the hero awoke. Whipping out his hunting-sword, " To arms! to arms! " he roared to the passengers; and away he flew, the foremost of all, upon the buccaneers.

" *Ques aco!* What's up? What's the matter with you? " exclaimed Captain Barbassou, coming out of the 'tweendecks.

" About time you did turn up, captain! Quick, quick, arm your men! "

" Eh, what for, dash it all! "

" Why, can't you see? "

" See what? "

" There, before you, the corsairs " —

Captain Barbassou stared, bewildered. At this juncture a tall blackamoor tore by with our hero's medicine-chest upon his back.

" You cut-throat! just wait for me! " yelled the Tarasconer as he sprung after him with knife uplifted.

But Barbassou caught him in the spring, and holding him by the waist-sash, bade him be quiet.

"*Tron de ler!* they're no pirates. It's long since there were any pirates hereabout. Those dark porters are light porters. Ha, Ha!"

"P-p-porters?"

"Rather, only come after the luggage to carry it ashore. So put up your cook's galley knife, give me your ticket, and walk off behind that nigger — an honest dog, who will see you to land, and even into a hotel, if you like."

A little abashed, Tartarin handed over his ticket, and falling in behind the representative of the Dark Continent, clambered down by the hanging-ladder into a big skiff dancing alongside. All his effects were already there — boxes, trunks, gun-cases, tinned food,— so cramming up the boat that there was no need to wait for any other passengers. The African scrambled upon the boxes, and squatted there like a baboon, with his knees clutched by his hands. Another negro took the oars. Both laughingly eyed Tartarin, and showed their white teeth.

Standing in the stern-sheets, making that terrifying face which had daunted his fellow-countrymen, the great Tarasconian feverishly fumbled with his hunting-knife haft; for, despite what Barbassou had told him, he was only half at ease as regarded the intention of these ebony-skinned porters, who so little resembled their honest mates of Tarascon.

Five minutes afterwards the skiff landed Tartarin, and he set foot upon the little Barbary wharf, where, three hundred years before, a Spanish galley-slave,

yclept Miguel Cervantes devised, under the cane of the
Algerian taskmaster, a sublime romance which was to
bear the title of " Don Quixote." . . .

"Blidah! Blidah!" called out the guard as he
opened the door.

Vaguely through the mud-dimmed glass Tartarin of
Tarascon caught a glimpse of a second-rate but pretty
town market-place, regular in shape, surrounded by
colonnades and planted with orange-trees, in the midst
of which what seemed toy leaden soldiers were going
through the morning exercise in the clear roseate mist.
The cafés were shedding their shutters. In one corner
there was a vegetable market. It was bewitching, but
it did not smack of lions yet.

"To the South! farther to the South!" muttered the good old desperado, sinking back in his
corner.

At this moment the door opened. A puff of fresh
air rushed in, bearing upon its wings, in the perfume
of the orange blossoms, a little person in a brown
frock-coat, old and dry, wrinkled and formal, his face
no bigger than your fist, his neckcloth of black silk five
fingers wide, a notary's letter-case, and umbrella — the
very picture of a village solicitor.

On perceiving the Tarasconian's warlike equipment,
the little gentleman, who was seated over against him,
appeared excessively surprised, and set to studying him
with burdensome persistency.

The horses were taken out and the fresh ones put in,
whereupon the coach started off again. The little
weasel still gazed at Tartarin, who in the end took
snuff at it.

"Does this astonish you?" he demanded, staring the little gentleman full in the face in his turn.

"Oh, dear no! it only annoys me," responded the other very tranquilly.

And the fact is, that, with his shelter-tent, revolvers, pair of guns in their cases, and hunting-knife, not to speak of his natural corpulence, Tartarin of Tarascon did take up a lot of room.

The little gentleman's reply angered him.

"Do you by any chance fancy that I am going lion hunting with your umbrella?" queried the great man haughtily.

The little man looked at his umbrella, smiled blandly, and still with the same lack of emotion, inquired : —

"Oho, then you are Monsieur " ——

"Tartarin of Tarascon, lion-killer!"

In uttering these words the dauntless son of Tarascon shook the blue tassel of his fez like a mane.

Through the vehicle was a spell of stupefaction.

The Trappist brother crossed himself, the dubious women uttered little screams of affright, and the Orléansville photographer bent over towards the lion-slayer, already cherishing the unequalled honor of taking his likeness.

The little gentleman, though, was not awed.

"Do you mean to say that you have killed many lions, Monsieur Tartarin?" he asked, very quietly.

The Tarasconian received his charge in the handsomest manner.

"Is it many have I killed, Monsieur? I wish you had only as many hairs on your head as I have killed of them."

All the coach laughed on observing three yellow bristles standing up on the little gentleman's skull.

In his turn the Orléansville photographer struck in: —

"Yours must be a terrible profession, Monsieur Tartarin. You must pass some ugly moments sometimes. I have heard that poor Monsieur Bombonnel" —

"Oh, yes, the panther-killer," said Tartarin, rather disdainfully.

"Do you happen to be acquainted with him?" inquired the insignificant person.

"Eh! of course! Know him? Why, we have been out on the hunt over twenty times together."

The little gentleman smiled.

"So you also hunt panthers, Monsieur Tartarin?" he asked.

"Sometimes, just for pastime," said the fiery Tarasconian. "But," he added, as he tossed his head with a heroic movement that inflamed the hearts of the two sweethearts of the regiment, "that's not worth lion-hunting."

"When all's said and done," ventured the photographer, "a panther is nothing but a big cat."

"Right you are!" said Tartarin, not sorry to abate the celebrated Bombonnel's glory a little, particularly in the presence of ladies.

Here the coach stopped. The conductor came to open the door, and addressed the insignificant little gentleman most respectfully, saying: —

"We have arrived, Monsieur."

The little gentleman got up, stepped out, and said before the door was closed again: —

"Will you allow me to give you a bit of advice, Monsieur Tartarin?"

"What is it, Monsieur?"

"Faith! you wear the look of a good sort of fellow, so I would, rather than not, let you have it. Get you back quickly to Tarascon, Monsieur Tartarin, for you are wasting your time here. There do remain a few panthers in the colony, but out upon the big cats! they are too small game for you. As for lion-hunting, that's all over. There are none left in Algeria, my friend Chassaing having lately knocked over the last."

MONSIEUR BOMBONNEL.

Upon which the little gentleman saluted, closed the door, and trotted away chuckling, with his document-wallet and umbrella.

"Guard," asked Tartarin, screwing up his face contemptuously, "who under the sun is that poor little mannikin?"

"What! don't you know him? Why, that there's Monsieur Bombonnel!"

At Milianah, Tartarin of Tarascon alighted, leaving the stage-coach to continue its way towards the South.

Two days' rough journey, two nights spent with eyes

open to spy out of window if there were not discoverable the dread figure of a lion in the fields beyond the road — so much sleeplessness well deserved some hours' repose. Besides, if we must tell everything, since his misadventure with Bombonnel, the outspoken Tartarin felt ill at ease, notwithstanding his weapons, his terrifying visage and his red cap, before the Orléansville photographer and the two ladies fond of the military.

So he proceeded through the broad streets of Milianah, full of fine trees and fountains; but whilst looking up a suitable hotel, the poor fellow could not help musing over Bombonnel's words. Suppose they were true! Suppose there were no more lions in Algeria! What would be the good, then, of so much running about and fatigue?

Suddenly, at the turn of a street, our hero found himself face to face with — with what? Guess! "A donkey, of course!" A donkey? A splendid lion this time, waiting before a coffee-house door, royally sitting up on his hindquarters, with his tawny mane gleaming in the sun.

"HUMBLY HELD IT OUT."

"What possessed them to tell me that there were no more of them?" exclaimed the Tarasconian, as he made a backward jump.

On hearing this outcry the lion lowered his head,

and taking up in his mouth a wooden bowl that was before him on the footway, humbly held it out towards Tartarin, who was immovable with stupefaction. A passing Arab tossed a copper into the bowl, and the lion wagged his tail. Thereupon Tartarin understood all. He saw what emotion had prevented him previously perceiving : that the crowd was gathered around a poor tame, blind lion, and that two stalwart negroes, armed with staves, were marching him through the town as a Savoyard does a marmot.

The blood of Tarascon boiled over at once.

"Wretches that you are!" he roared in a voice of thunder, "thus to debase such noble beasts!"

Springing to the lion, he wrenched the loathsome bowl from between his royal jaws. The two Africans, believing they had a thief to contend with, rushed upon the foreigner with uplifted cudgels. There was a dreadful conflict : the blackamoors smiting, the women screaming, and the youngsters laughing. An old Jew cobbler bleated out of the hollow of his stall, "Dake him to the shustish of the beace!" The lion himself, in his dark state, tried to roar as his hapless champion, after a desperate struggle, rolled on the ground among the spilt pence and the sweepings.

At this juncture a man cleft the throng, made the negroes stand back with a word, and the women and urchins with a wave of the hand, lifted up Tartarin, brushed him down, shook him into shape, and sat him breathless upon a corner-post.

"What, prince, is it you?" said the good Tartarin, rubbing his ribs.

"Yes, indeed, it is I, my valiant friend. As soon as

your letter was received, I entrusted Baya to her brother, hired a post-chaise, flew fifty leagues as fast as a horse could go, and here I am, just in time to snatch you from the brutality of these ruffians. What have you done, in the name of just Heaven, to bring this ugly trouble upon you ? "

" What done, prince ? It was too much for me to see this unfortunate lion with a begging-bowl in his mouth, humiliated, conquered, buffeted about, set up as a laughing-stock to all this Moslem rabble " —

" But you are wrong, my noble friend. On the contrary, this lion is an object of respect and adoration. This is a sacred beast who belongs to a great monastery of lions, founded three hundred years ago by Mahomet Ben Aouda, a kind of fierce and forbidding La Trappe ; full of roarings and wild-beastly odors, where strange monks rear and feed lions by hundreds, and send them out all over Northern Africa, accompanied by begging brothers. The alms they receive serve for the maintenance of the monastery and its mosque ; and the two negroes showed so much displeasure just now because it was their conviction that the lion under their charge would forthwith devour them if a single penny of their collection were lost or stolen through any fault of theirs."

On hearing this incredible and yet veracious story Tartarin of Tarascon was delighted, and sniffed the air noisily.

" What pleases me in this," he remarked, as the summing up of his opinion, " is that, whether Monsieur Bombonnel likes it or not, there are still lions in Algeria " —

"I should think there were!" ejaculated the prince enthusiastically. "We will start to-morrow beating up the Shelliff Plain, and you will see lions enough!"

"What, prince! have you an intention to go a-hunting, too?"

"Of course! Do you think I am going to leave you to march by yourself into the heart of Africa, in the midst of ferocious tribes of whose languages and usages you are ignorant? No, no, illustrious Tartarin, I shall quit you no more. Go where you will, I shall make one of the party."

"O prince! prince!"

The beaming Tartarin hugged the devoted Gregory to his breast at the proud thought of his going to have a foreign prince to accompany him in his hunting, after the example of Jules Gérard, Bombonnel, and other famous lion-slayers.

Leaving Milianah at the earliest hour next morning, the intrepid Tartarin and the no less intrepid Prince Gregory descended towards the Shelliff Plain through a delightful gorge shaded with jessamine, carouba, tuyas, and wild-olive trees, between hedges of little native gardens and thousands of merry, lively rills, which scampered down from rock to rock with a singing splash — a bit of landscape meet for the Lebanon.

As much loaded with arms as the great Tartarin, Prince Gregory had, over and above that, donned a queer but magnificent military cap, all covered with gold lace and a trimming of oak-leaves in silver cord, which gave His Highness the aspect of a Mexican general or a railway station-master on the banks of the Danube.

This plague of a cap much puzzled the beholder; and as he timidly craved some explanation, the prince gravely answered : —

"It is a kind of headgear indispensable for travel in Algeria."

Whilst brightening up the peak with a sweep of his sleeve, he instructed his simple companion in the important part which the military cap plays in the French connection with the Arabs, and the terror this article of army insignia alone has the privilege of inspiring, so that the Civil Service has been obliged to put all its employees in caps, from the extra-copyist to the receiver-general. To govern Algeria (the prince is still speaking) there is no need of a strong head, or even of any head at all. A military cap does it alone, if showy and belaced, and shining at the top of a non-human *pole*, like Gessler's.

Thus chatting and philosophizing, the caravan proceeded. The barefooted porters leaped from rock to rock with ape-like screams. The gun-cases clanked, and the guns themselves flashed. The natives who were passing, salaamed to the ground before the magic cap. Up above, on the ramparts of Milianah, the head of the Arab Department, who was out for an airing with his wife, hearing these unusual noises, and seeing the weapons gleam between the branches, fancied there was a revolt, and ordered the drawbridge to be raised, the general alarm to be sounded, and the whole town put under a state of siege.

A capital commencement for the caravan!

Unfortunately, before the day ended, things went wrong. Of the black luggage-bearers, one was doubled up with atrocious colics from having eaten the diachylon out of the medicine-chest; another fell on the roadside dead drunk with camphorated brandy; the third carrier of the travelling-album, deceived by the gilding on the clasps into the persuasion that he was flying with the treasures of Mecca, ran off into the Zaccar on his best legs.

This required consideration. The caravan halted, and held a counsel in the broken shadow of an old fig-tree.

"It's my advice that we turn up negro porters from this evening forward," said the prince, trying without success to melt a cake of compressed meat in an improved patent triple-bottomed sauce-pan. "There is, haply, an Arab trader quite near here. The best thing to do is to stop there, and buy some donkeys."

"No, no; no donkeys," quickly interrupted Tartarin, becoming quite red at memory of Noiraud. "How can you expect," he added, hypocrite that he was, "that such little beasts could carry all our apparatus?"

The prince smiled.

"You are making a mistake, my illustrious friend. However weakly and meagre the Algerian *bourriquot* may appear to you, he has solid loins. He must have them so to support all that he does. Just ask the Arabs. Hark to how they explain the French Colonial organization. 'On the top,' they say, 'is Mossoo, the Governor, with a heavy club to rap the staff; the staff, for revenge, canes the soldier; the soldier clubs the settler, and he hammers the Arab; the Arab smites the negro, the negro beats the Jew, and he takes it out of the donkey. The poor *bourriquot*, having nobody to belabor, arches up his back and bears it all.' You see clearly now that he can bear your boxes."

"All the same," remonstrated Tartarin, "it strikes me that jackasses will not chime in nicely with the effect of our caravan. I want something more Oriental. For instance, if we could only get a camel" —

"As many as you like," said His Highness; and off they started for the Arab mart.

It was held a few miles away, on the banks of the Shelliff. There were five or six thousand Arabs in tatters here, grovelling in the sunshine and noisily trafficking, amid jars of black olives, pots of honey, bags of spices, and great heaps of cigars; huge fires were roasting whole sheep, basted with butter; in open-air slaughter-houses stark naked negroes, with ruddy arms and their feet in gore, were cutting up kids hanging from crosspoles, with small knives.

In one corner, under a tent patched with a thousand colors, a Moorish clerk of the market in spectacles scrawled in a large book. Here was a cluster of men shouting with rage: it was a spinning-jenny game, set on a corn-measure, and Kabyles were ready to cut one another's throats over it. Yonder were laughs and contortions of delight: it was a Jew trader on a mule drowning in the Shelliff. Then there were dogs, scorpions, ravens, and flies — more flies than anything else.

But a plentiful lack of camels abounded. They finally unearthed one, though, of which the M'zabites were trying to get rid — the real ship of the desert, the classical, standard camel, bald, woe-begone, with a long Bedouin head, and its hump become limp in consequence of unduly long fasts, hanging melancholily on one side.

Tartarin considered it so handsome that he wanted the entire party to get upon it. Still his Oriental craze!

The beast knelt down for them to strap on the boxes.

The prince enthroned himself on the animal's neck. For the sake of the greater majesty, Tartarin got them to hoist him on the top of the hump between two boxes, where, proud, and cosily settled down, he saluted the whole market with a lofty wave of the hand, and gave the signal of departure.

Thunderation! if the people of Tarascon could only have seen him!

The camel rose, straightened up its long, knotty legs and stepped out.

Oh, stupor! At the end of a few strides Tartarin felt he was losing color, and the heroic *chechia* assumed one by one its former positions in the days of sailing in the Zouave. This devil's own camel pitched and tossed like a frigate.

"Prince! prince!" gasped Tartarin, pallid as a ghost, as he clung to the dry tuft of the hump, "Prince, let's get down. I find—I feel that I m-m-must get off, or I shall disgrace France."

A deal of good that talk was—the camel was on the go, and nothing could stop it. Behind it raced four thousand barefooted Arabs, waving their hands and laughing like mad, so that they made six hundred thousand white teeth glitter in the sun.

The great man of Tarascon had to resign himself to circumstances. He sadly collapsed on the hump, where the fez took all the positions it fancied, and France was disgraced.

Sweetly picturesque as was their new steed, our lion-hunters had to give it up, purely out of consideration for the red cap, of course. So they continued the journey on foot as before, the caravan tranquilly proceeding southwardly by short stages, the Tarasconian in the van, the Montenegrin in the rear, and the camel, with the weapons in their cases, in the ranks.

The expedition lasted nearly a month. . . .

But still no lions, no more than on London Bridge.

Nevertheless, the Tarasconian did not grow disheartened. Ever bravely diving more deeply into the South, he spent the days in beating up the thickets, probing the dwarf-palms with the muzzle of his rifle, and saying "Boh!" to every bush. And every evening, before lying down, he went into ambush for two or three hours. Useless trouble, however, for the lion did not show himself.

One evening, though, going on six o'clock, as the caravan scrambled through a violet-hued mastic-grove, where fat quails tumbled about in the grass, drowsy through the heat, Tartarin of Tarascon fancied he heard — though afar and very vague, and thinned down by the breeze — that wondrous roaring to which he had so often listened by Mitaine's Menagerie at home.

At first the hero feared he was dreaming; but in an instant further the roaring recommenced more distinct, although yet remote; and this time the camel's hump shivered in terror, and made the tinned meats and arms in the cases rattle, whilst all the dogs in the camps were heard howling in every corner of the horizon.

Beyond doubt this was the lion.

Quick! Quick! to the ambush. There was not a minute to lose.

Near at hand there happened to be an old *marabout* or saint's tomb, with a white cupola, and the defunct's large yellow slippers placed in a niche over the door, and a mass of odd offerings — hems of blankets, gold thread, red hair — hung on the wall.

Tartarin of Tarascon left his prince and his camel and went in search of a good spot for lying in wait. Prince Gregory wanted to follow him, but the Tarasconian refused, bent on confronting Leo alone. But still he besought His Highness not to go too far away, and, as a measure of foresight, he entrusted him with his pocket-book, a good-sized one, full of precious papers and bank-notes, which he feared would get torn by the lion's claws. This done, our hero looked up a good place.

A hundred steps in front of the temple a little clump of rose-laurel shook in the twilight haze on the edge of a rivulet all but dried up. Thither went Tartarin and took his position, one knee on the ground, according to the regular rule, his rifle in his hand, and his huge hunting-knife stuck boldly before him in the sandy bank.

Night fell.

The rosy tint of nature changed into violet, and then into dark blue. A pretty pool of clear water gleamed like a hand-glass over the river-pebbles; this was the watering-place of the wild animals.

On the other slope the whitish trail was dimly to be discerned which their heavy paws had traced in the bush

—a mysterious path which made one's flesh creep. Join to this sensation that from the vague swarming sound in African forests, the swishing of branches, the velvety pads of roving creatures, the jackal's shrill yelp, and up in the sky, two or three hundred feet aloft, vast flocks of cranes passing on with screams like poor little children having their weasands slit. You will own that there were grounds for a man being moved.

Tartarin was moved: the poor fellow's teeth chattered, and on the cross-bar of his hunting-knife, planted upright in the bank, as we repeat, his rifle-barrel rattled

"HIS KNIFE PLANTED UPRIGHT."

like a pair of castanets. Do not ask too much of a man! There are times when one is not in the mood; and, moreover, where would be the merit if heroes were never afraid?

Well, yes, Tartarin was afraid, and all the time, too, for the matter of that. Nevertheless he held out for an hour; better, for two; but heroism has its limits. Nigh him, in the dry part of the rivulet-bed, the Tarasconian unexpectedly heard the sound of steps and of pebbles rolling. This time terror lifted him off the ground. He banged away both barrels at hap-hazard into the night, and retreated as fast as his legs would carry him to the *marabout's* chapel-vault, leaving his knife standing up in the sand like a cross commemorative of the grandest panic that ever assailed the soul of a conqueror of hydras.

"Help! this way, prince; the lion is on me!"

There was silence.

"Prince, prince, are you there?"

The prince was not there. On the white moonlit wall of the fane the camel alone cast the queer-shaped shadow of protuberance. Prince Gregory had cut and run with the wallet of bank-notes. His Highness had been for the month past awaiting this opportunity.

Not until early on the morrow of this adventurous and dramatic eve did our hero awake and acquire assurance doubly sure that the prince and the treasure had really gone off, without any prospect of return. When he saw himself alone in the little white tomb-house, betrayed, robbed, abandoned in the heart of savage Algeria, with a one-humped camel and some pocket-money as all his resources, then did the representative of Tarascon for the first time doubt. He doubted Montenegro, friendship, glory, and even lions; and the great man blubbered bitterly.

Whilst he was pensively seated on the sill of the sanctuary, holding his head between his hands and his gun between his legs, with the camel mooning at him, the thicket over the way was divided, and the stupor-stricken Tartarin saw a gigantic lion appear not a dozen paces off. It thrust out its high head and emitted powerful roars, which made the temple walls shake beneath their votive decorations, and even the saint's slippers dance in their niche.

The Tarasconian alone did not tremble.

"At last you've come!" he shouted, jumping up and leveling the rifle.

Bang, bang! went a brace of shells into its head.

It was done. For a minute, on the fiery background of the Afric sky, there was a dreadful firework display of scattered brains, smoking blood and tawny hair. When all fell, Tartarin perceived two colossal negroes furiously running towards him, brandishing cudgels. They were his two negro acquaintances of Milianah!

Oh, misery!

This was the domesticated lion, the poor blind beggar of the Mohammed Monastery, whom the Tarasconian's bullets had knocked over.

This time, in spite of Mahound, Tartarin escaped neatly. Drunk with fanatical fury, the two African collectors would have surely beaten him to pulp had not the god of chase and war sent him a delivering angel in the shape of the rural constable of the Orléansville commune. By a bypath this *garde champêtre* came up, his sword tucked under his arm.

The sight of the municipal cap suddenly calmed the negroes' choler. Peaceful and majestic, the officer with the brass badge drew up a report on the affair, ordered the camel to be loaded with what remained of the king of beasts, and the plaintiffs as well as the delinquent to follow him, proceeding to Orléansville, where all was deposited with the law-courts receiver.

There issued a long and alarming case! . . .

The puzzle lay in the limitation of the two territories being very hazy in Algeria.

At length, after a month's running about, entanglements, and waiting under the sun in the yards of Arab Departmental offices, it was established that, whereas the lion had been killed on the military territory, on the other hand Tartarin was in the civil territory when he shot. So the case was decided in the civil courts, and our hero was let off on paying two thousand five hundred francs damages, costs not included.

How could he pay such a sum?

The few piastres escaped from the prince's sweep had long since gone in legal documents and judicial libations. The unfortunate lion-destroyer was therefore reduced to selling the store of guns by retail, rifle by rifle; so went the daggers, the Malay kreeses, and the life-preservers. A grocer purchased the preserved aliments; an apothecary what remained of the medicaments. The big boots themselves walked off after the improved tent to a dealer of curiosities who elevated them to the dignity of " rarities from Cochin-China."

When everything was paid up, only the lion's skin and the camel remained to Tartarin. The hide he had carefully packed, to be sent to Tarascon to the address of brave Commandant Bravida, and, later on, we shall see what came of this fabulous trophy. As for the camel, he reckoned on making use of him to get back to Algiers, not by riding on him, but by selling him to pay his coach-fare — the best way to employ a camel in travelling. Unhappily the beast was difficult to place and no one would offer a copper for him.

Still Tartarin wanted to regain Algiers by hook or

crook. . . . So our hero did not hesitate; distressed but not downcast, he undertook to make the journey afoot and penniless by short stages.

In this enterprise the camel did not cast him off. The strange animal had taken an unaccountable fancy for his master, and on seeing him leave Orléansville, he set to striding steadfastly behind him, regulating his pace by his, and never quitting him by a yard.

At the first outset Tartarin found this touching; such fidelity and devotion above proof went to his heart, all the more because the creature was accommodating, and fed himself on nothing. Nevertheless, after a few days, the Tarasconian was worried by having his glum companion perpetually at his heels, to remind him of his misadventures. Ire arising, he hated him for his sad aspect, hump and gait of a goose in harness. To tell the whole truth, he held him as his Old Man of the Sea, and only pondered on how to shake him off; but the follower would not be shaken off. Tartarin attempted to lose him, but the camel always found him; he tried to outrun him, but the camel ran faster. He bade him begone, and hurled stones at him. The camel stopped with a mournful mien, but in a minute resumed the pursuit, and always ended by overtaking him. Tartarin had to resign himself.

For all that, when, after a full week of tramping, the dusty and harassed Tarasconian espied the first white housetops of Algiers glimmer from afar in the verdure, and when he got to the city gates on the noisy Mustapha Avenue, amid the Zouaves, Biskris, and Mahonnais, all swarming around him and staring at him trudging by with his camel, overtasked patience escaped him.

"No! no!" he growled, "it is not likely! I cannot enter Algiers with such an animal!"

Profiting by a jam of vehicles, he turned off into the fields and jumped into a ditch. In a minute or so he saw over his head on the highway, the camel flying off with long strides and stretching his neck with a wistful air.

Relieved of a great weight thereby, the hero sneaked out of his covert, and entered the town anew by a circuitous path which skirted the wall of his own little garden. . . .

"You'd best cut back to Tarascon at full speed," said Captain Barbassou.

"It's easy to say, 'Cut back.' Where's the money to come from? Don't you know that I was plucked out there in the desert?"

"What does that matter?" said the captain merrily. "The Zouave sails to-morrow, and if you like I will take you home. Does that suit you, mate? Ay? Then all goes well. You have only one thing to do. There are some bottles of fizz left, and half the pie. Sit you down and pitch in without any grudge."

After the minute's wavering which self-respect commanded, the Tarasconian chose his course manfully. Down he sat, and they touched glasses. Baya, gliding down at that chink, sang the finale of "Marco la Bella," and the jollification was prolonged deep into the night.

About 3 A.M., with a light head, but a heavy foot, our good Tarasconian was returning from seeing his friend the captain off, when, in passing the mosque, the remembrance of his muezzin and his practical jokes made him laugh, and instantly a capital idea of revenge flitted through his brain.

The door was open. He entered, threaded long corridors hung with mats, mounted and kept on mounting till he finally found himself in a little oratory, where an openwork iron lantern swung from the ceiling, and embroidered an odd pattern in shadows upon the blanched walls.

There sat the crier on the divan, in his large turban and white pelisse, with his Mostaganam pipe, and a bumper of absinthe before him, which he whipped up in the orthodox manner, whilst awaiting the hour to call true believers to prayer. At view of Tartarin, he dropped his pipe in terror.

"Not a word, knave!" said the Tarasconian, full of his project. "Quick! Off with turban and coat!"

The Turkish priest-crier tremblingly handed over his outer garments, as he would have done with anything else. Tartarin donned them, and gravely stepped out upon the minaret platform.

In the distance the sea shone. The white roofs glittered in the moonbeams. On the sea breeze was heard the strumming of a few belated guitars. For a space the Tarasconian muezzin gathered himself up for the effort, and then, raising his arms, he set to chanting in a very shrill voice:

"*La Allah il Allah!* Mahomet is an old humbug! The Orient, the Koran, bashaws, lions, Moorish beauties — they are all not worth a fly's skip! There is nothing left but gammoners. Long live Tarascon!"

Whilst the illustrious Tartarin, in his queer jumbling of Arabic and Provençal, flung his mirthful maledictions to the four quarters, sea, town, plain and mountain, the clear, solemn voices of the other muezzins answered him, taking up the strain from minaret to minaret, and the believers of the upper town devoutly beat their bosoms.

The Zouave had her steam up, ready to sail.

Tartarin of Tarascon had no luggage. Here he comes down the Rue de la Marine through the little market, full of bananas and melons, accompanied by his friend Barbassou. The hapless Tarasconian left on the Moorish strand his gun-cases and his illusions, and now he had to sail for Tarascon with his hands in his otherwise empty pockets. He had barely leaped into the captain's cutter before a breathless beast slid down from the heights of the square and galloped towards him. It was the faithful camel, who had been hunting after his master in Algiers during the last four-and-twenty hours.

On seeing him, Tartarin changed countenance, and feigned not to know him, but the camel was not going to be put off. He scampered along the quay; he whinnied for his friend, and regarded him with affection.

"Take me away," his sad eyes seemed to say, "take me away in your ship, far, far from this sham Arabia, this ridiculous Land of the East, full of locomotives and stage coaches, where a camel is so sorely out of keeping that I do not know what will become of me. You are the last real Turk, and I am the last camel. Do not let us part, O my Tartarin!"

"Is that camel yours?" the captain inquired.

"Not at all!" replied Tartarin, who shuddered at the idea of entering Tarascon with that ridiculous escort; and, impudently denying the companion of his misfortunes, he spurned the Algerian soil with his foot, and gave the cutter the shoving-off start. The camel sniffed of the water, extended its neck, cracked its joints, and, jumping in behind the row-boat at haphazard, he swam towards the Zouave with his humpback floating like a bladder, and his long neck projecting over the wave like the beak of a galley.

Cutter and camel came alongside the mail steamer together.

"This dromedary regularly cuts me up," observed Captain Barbassou, quite affected. "I have a good mind to take him aboard and make a present of him to the Zoölogical Gardens at Marseilles."

And so they hauled up the camel with many blocks and tackles upon the deck, being increased in weight by the brine, and the Zouave started.

From hour to hour, through the cabin port-holes, where he stuck out his nose now and then, Tartarin saw the Algerian blue sky pale away; until one morning, in a silvery fog, he heard with delight Marseilles bells ringing out. The Zouave had arrived and cast anchor.

Our hero, having no luggage, got off, without saying anything, hastily slipped through Marseilles for fear he was still pursued by the camel, and never breathed till he was in a third-class carriage making for Tarascon.

Deceptive security!

Hardly were they two leagues from the city before every head was stuck out of window. There were outcries and astonishment. Tartarin looked in his turn, and — what did he descry! the camel, reader, the inevitable camel, racing along the line behind the train, and keeping up with it! The dismayed Tartarin drew back and shut his eyes.

After this disastrous expedition of his he had reckoned on slipping into his house *incognito*. But the presence of this burdensome quadruped rendered the thing impossible. What kind of a triumphal entry would he make? Good heavens! not a sou, not a lion, nothing to show for it save a camel!

" Tarascon! Tarascon!"

He was obliged to get down.

O amazement!

Scarcely had the hero's red fez popped out of the doorway before a loud shout of " Tartarin forever!" made the glazed roof of the railway station tremble. " Long life to Tartarin, the lion-slayer!" And out burst the windings of horns and the choruses of the local musicial societies.

Tartarin felt death had come: he believed it was a hoax. But, no! all Tarascon was there, waving their hats, all of the same way of thinking. Behold the brave Commandant Bravida, Costecalde the armorer, the Chief Judge, the chemist, and the whole noble corps of cap-poppers, who pressed around their leader, and carried him in triumph out through the passages.

Singular effects of the mirage! — the hide of the blind lion sent to Bravida was the cause of all this riot. With that humble fur exhibited in the club-room, the

Tarasconians, and, at the back of them, the whole
South of France, had grown exalted. The *Semaphore*
newspaper had spoken of it. A drama had been invented. It was not merely a solitary lion which Tartarin had slain, but ten, nay, twenty — pooh ! a herd
of lions had been made marmalade of. Hence, on dis-
embarking at Marseilles, Tartarin was already celebrated without being aware of it, and an enthusiastic
telegram had gone on before him by two hours to his
native place.

But what capped the climax of the popular gladness
was to see a fancifully shaped animal, covered with
foam and dust, appear behind the hero, and stumble
down the station stairs.

Tarascon for an instant believed that its dragon was
come again.

Tartarin set his fellow-citizens at ease.

" This is my camel," he said.

Already feeling the influence of the splendid sun of
Tarascon, which makes people tell " bouncers " unwit-
tingly, he added, as he fondled the camel's hump : —

" It is a noble beast ! It saw me kill all my lions ! "

THE YARN OF THE NANCY BELL

(From the Bab Ballads.)

By WILLIAM S. GILBERT.

'TWAS on the shores that round our coast
From Deal to Ramsgate span,
That I found alone, on a piece of stone,
An elderly naval man.

His hair was weedy, his beard was long,
And weedy and long was he,
And I heard this wight on the shore recite,
In a singular minor key:

" Oh, I am a cook and a captain bold,
And the mate of the Nancy brig,
And a bo'sun tight, and a
midshipmite,
And the crew of the
captain's gig."

And he shook his fists and
he tore his hair,
Till I really felt afraid ;
"An Elderly Naval Man."   For I couldn't help think-
ing the man had been drinking,
And so I simply said :

"An Elderly Naval Man."

310

" Oh, elderly man, it's little I know
    Of the duties of men of the sea,
And I'll eat my hand if I understand
    How you can possibly be

At once a cook, and a captain bold,
    And the mate of the Nancy brig,
And a bo'sun tight and a midshipmite,
    And the crew of the captain's gig."

Then he gave a hitch to his trousers, which
    Is a trick all seamen larn,
And having got rid of a thumping quid,
    He spun this painful yarn :

" 'Twas in the good ship Nancy Bell
    That we sailed to the Indian sea,
And there on a reef we came to grief,
    Which has often occurred to me.

And pretty nigh all o' the crew was drowned
    (There was seventy-seven o' soul),
And only ten of the Nancy's men
    Said ' Here ! ' to the muster roll.

There was me and the cook and the captain bold,
    And the mate of the Nancy brig,
And the bo'sun tight and a midshipmite,
    And the crew of the captain's gig.

For a month we'd neither wittles nor drink,
    Till a-hungry we did feel,
So, we drawed a lot, and, accordin' shot
    The captain for our meal.

The next lot fell to the Nancy's mate,
    And a delicate dish he made;
Then our appetite with the midshipmite
    We seven survivors stayed.

And then we murdered the bo'sun tight,
    And he much resembled pig;
Then we wittled free, did the cook and me,
    On the crew of the captain's gig.

Then only the cook and me was left,
    And the delicate question, 'Which
Of us two goes to the kettle?' arose,
    And we argued it out as sich.

For I loved that cook as a brother, I did,
    And the cook he worshipped me;
But we'd both be blowed if we'd either be stowed
    In the other chap's hold, you see.

'I'll be eat if you dines off me,' says Tom,
    'Yes, that,' says I, 'you'll be,'—
'I'm boiled if I die, my friend,' quoth I,
    'And 'Exactly so,' quoth he.

Says he, 'Dear James, to murder me
    Were a foolish thing to do,
For don't you see that you can't cook *me*,
    While I can — and will — cook *you!*'

So he boils the water, and takes the salt
    And the pepper in portions true
(Which he never forgot), and some chopped shalot,
    And some sage and parsley too.

'Come here,' says he, with a proper pride,
  Which his smiling features tell,
"'Twill soothing be if I let you see,
  How extremely nice you'll smell.'

And he stirred it round and round and round,
  And he sniffed the foaming froth;
When I ups with his heels, and smothers his squeal
  In the scum of the boiling broth.

And I eat that cook in a week or less,
  And — as I eating be
The last of his chops, why I almost drops,
  For a wessel in sight I see.

          .   .   .   .

And I never larf, and I never smile,
  And I never lark nor play,
But I set and croak, and a single joke
  I have — which is to say:

Oh, I am a cook and a captain bold,
  And the mate of the Nancy brig,
And a bo'sun tight, and a midshipmite,
  And the crew of the captain's gig!"

THE HIGHLY RESPECTABLE GON-
DOLIER

(FROM THE BAB BALLADS.)

By WILLIAM S. GILBERT.

I STOLE the Prince, and I brought him here,
    And left him, gayly prattling
With a highly respectable Gondolier,
Who promised the Royal babe to rear,
And teach him the trade of a timoneer
    With his own beloved bratling.

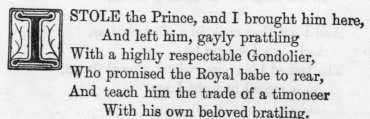

Both of the babes were strong and
    stout,
    And, considering all things, clever.
Of that there is no manner of doubt —
    No probable, possi-
      ble shadow of
      doubt —
    No possible doubt
      whatever.

Time sped, and when
    at the end of a
    year
    I sought that in-
    fant cherished,

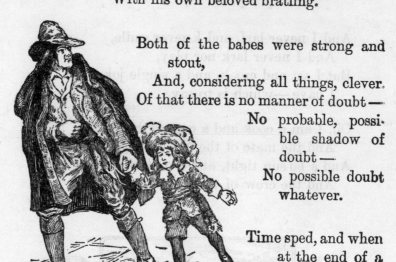

"I STOLE THE PRINCE."

314

That highly respectable Gondolier
Was lying a corpse on his humble bier —
I dropped a Grand Inquisitor's tear —
    That Gondolier had perished.

A taste for drink, combined with gout,
    Had doubled him up for ever.
Of *that* there is no manner of doubt —
No probable, possible shadow of doubt —
    No possible doubt whatever.

But owing, I'm much disposed to fear,
    To his terrible taste for tippling,
That highly respected Gondolier
Could never declare with a mind sincere
Which of the two was his offspring dear,
    And which the Royal stripling!

Which was which he could never make out,
    Despite his best endeavor.
Of *that* there is no manner of doubt —
No probable, possible shadow of doubt —
    No possible doubt whatever.

The children followed his old career —
    (This statement can't be parried)
Of a highly respectable Gondolier:
Well, one of the two (who will soon be here) —
But *which* of the two is not quite clear —
    Is the Royal Prince you married!

Search in and out and round about
    And you'll discover never
A tale so free from every doubt —
All probable, possible shadow of doubt —
    All possible doubt whatever !